A2 Chemistry
UNITS 2815 & 2816

OCR

Module 2815: Trends and Patterns
Module 2816: Unifying Concepts in Chemistry

Mike Smith

Philip Allan Updates
Market Place
Deddington
Oxfordshire
OX15 0SE

tel: 01869 338652
fax: 01869 337590
e-mail: sales@philipallan.co.uk
www.philipallan.co.uk

ISBN 0 86003 893 9

This Guide has been written specifically to support students preparing for the OCR A2 Chemistry Unit 2815 and 2816 examinations. The content has been neither approved nor endorsed by OCR and remains the sole responsibility of the author.

Printed by Information Press, Eynsham, Oxford

P00121

Contents

Introduction

■ ■ ■

Content Guidance

■ ■ ■

Questions and Answers

Introduction

About this guide

This unit guide is written to help you to prepare for Component 01 of Unit Tests 2815 and 2816, which examine the content of **Module 2815: Trends and Patterns** and **Module 2816: Unifying Concepts in Chemistry**. This guide does not cover the optional units of Module 2815 or the practical component of Module 2816.

This **Introduction** provides advice on how to use the guide, together with suggestions for effective revision.

The **Content Guidance** section gives a point-by-point description of all the facts you need to know and concepts that you need to understand for Modules 2815 and 2816. It aims to provide you with a basis for your revision. However, you must also be prepared to use other sources in your preparation for the examination.

The **Question and Answer** section shows you the sort of questions you can expect in the unit test. It would be impossible to give examples of every kind of question in one book, but the questions used should give you a flavour of what to expect. Each question has been attempted by two candidates, Candidate A and Candidate B. Their answers, along with the examiner's comments, should help you to see what you need to do to score a good mark — and how you can easily *not* score marks, even though you probably understand the chemistry.

What can I assume about the guide?

You can assume that:
- the topics covered in the Content Guidance section relate directly to those in the specification
- the basic facts you need to know are stated clearly
- the major concepts you need to understand are explained
- the questions at the end of the guide are similar in style to those that will appear in the unit test
- the answers supplied are genuine, combining responses commonly written by candidates
- the standard of the marking is broadly equivalent to the standard that will be applied to your answers

What can I *not* assume about the guide?

You must *not* assume that:
- every last detail has been covered
- the way in which the concepts are explained is the *only* way they can be presented in an examination (often concepts are presented in an unfamiliar situation)

- the range of question types presented is exhaustive (examiners are always thinking of new ways to test a topic)

So how should I use this guide?

The guide lends itself to a number of uses throughout your course — it is not *just* a revision aid.

The Content Guidance is laid out in sections that correspond to those of the specification for Modules 2815 and 2816 so that you can:
- use it to check that your notes cover the material required by the specification
- use it to identify strengths and weaknesses
- use it as a reference for homework and internal tests
- use it during your revision to prepare 'bite-sized' chunks of material rather than being faced with a file full of notes

The Question and Answer section can be used to:
- identify the terms used by examiners in questions and what they expect of you
- familiarise yourself with the style of questions you can expect
- identify the ways in which marks are lost or gained

Study skills and revision techniques

All students need to develop good study skills. This section provides advice and guidance on how to study A2 chemistry.

Organising your notes

Chemistry students often accumulate a large quantity of notes, so it is useful to keep these in a well-ordered and logical manner. It is necessary to review your notes regularly, maybe rewriting the notes taken during lessons so that they are clear and concise, with key points highlighted. You should check your notes using textbooks and fill in any gaps. Make sure that you go back and ask your teacher if you are unsure about anything, especially if you find conflicting information in your class notes and textbook.

It is a good idea to file your notes in specification order using a consistent series of headings. The Content Guidance section can help you with this.

Organising your time

When organising your time, make sure that you plan carefully, allowing enough time to cover all of the work. It sounds easy, but it is one of the most difficult things to do. There is considerable evidence to show that revising for 2–3 hours at a time is counterproductive and that it is much better to work in short, sharp bursts of between 30 minutes and an hour.

Preparation for examinations is a very personal thing. Different people prepare, equally successfully, in very different ways. The key is being totally honest about what actually *works for you*.

Whatever your style, you must have a plan. Sitting down the night before the examination with a file full of notes and a textbook does not constitute a revision plan — it is just desperation — and you must not expect a great deal from it. Whatever your personal style, there are a number of things you *must* do and a number of other things you *could* do.

The **Trends and Patterns** and **Unifying Concepts in Chemistry** modules are very different. **Trends and Patterns** contains a lot of factual chemistry that has to be learnt, while **Unifying Concepts in Chemistry** requires understanding and the ability to apply that understanding to new situations.

The scheme outlined below is a suggestion as to how you might revise Trends and Patterns over a 3-week period. The work pattern shown is fairly simple. It involves revising and/or rewriting a topic and then over the next few days going through it repeatedly but never spending more than 30 minutes at a time. When you are confident that you have covered all areas, start trying to answer questions from past papers or this guide's Question and Answer section. Mark them yourself and seek help with anything that you are not sure about.

Day	Week 1	Week 2	Week 3
Mon	Topic 1(a) — Lattice enthalpy: review of enthalpy section from Module 2813 and Born–Haber cycles from this module Allow about 30 minutes	Reread all your summary notes at least twice	You have now revised all of Trends and Patterns and have attempted questions relating to each topic Make a list of your weaknesses and ask your teacher for help Reread all your summary notes at least twice Ask someone to test you
Tue	Topic 1(b) — Lattice enthalpy: factors affecting lattice enthalpy and thermal decomposition of carbonates Allow about 30 minutes, followed by 10 minutes rereading yesterday's notes on Topic 1(a)	Using past papers or other question sources, try a structured question on Topic 1 Mark it and list anything you do not understand Allow about 30 minutes	Using past papers or other question sources, try a relevant question that requires extended writing (essay-type question) from any of the topics Mark it and list anything you do not understand Allow about 30 minutes

Day	Week 1	Week 2	Week 3
Wed	Topic 2(a) — Period 3: redox reactions, period 3 compounds and their reactions with water Allow about 30 minutes, followed by 10 minutes rereading yesterday's notes on Topic 1(b) and 5 minutes going over Topic 1(a)	Using past papers or other question sources, try a structured question on Topic 2 Mark it and list anything you do not understand Allow about 30 minutes	Using past papers or other question sources, try a relevant question that requires extended writing (essay-type question) from any of the topics Mark it and list anything you do not understand Allow about 30 minutes
Thu	Topic 2(b) — Period 3: trends in structure and bonding Allow about 30 minutes, followed by 10 minutes reading yesterday's notes on Topic 2(a), 5 minutes going over Topic 1(b) and, finally, 2 minutes on Topic 1(a)	Using past papers or other question sources, try a structured question on Topic 3 Mark it and list anything you do not understand Allow about 30 minutes	Collect together about four structured questions and one extended answer question covering all three topics and try them under exam conditions Allow 45 minutes Mark them and list anything you do not understand
Fri	Topic 3(a) — Transition metals: general properties Allow about 30 minutes, followed by 10 minutes rereading yesterday's notes on Topic 2(b), 5 minutes going over Topic 2(a) and, finally, 2 minutes on Topic 1(b)	Using past papers or other question sources, try a structured question on each of the three topics Mark them and list anything you do not understand Allow about 45 minutes	Reread all your summary notes at least twice Concentrate on the weaknesses you identified on Monday (by now you should have talked to your teacher about them) Ask someone to test you
Sat	Topic 3(b) — Transition metals: colorimetry and redox reactions Allow about 30 minutes, followed by 10 minutes rereading yesterday's notes on Topic 3(a), 5 minutes going over Topics 2(b) and, finally, 2 minutes on Topic 2(a)	Using past papers or other question sources, try a structured question on each of the three topics Mark them and list anything you do not understand Allow about 45 minutes	Attempt a past exam paper Allow 1 hour Use your notes and other sources to mark your responses List anything you do not understand Plan to see your teacher for additional help with your weaknesses
Sun	Rest	Rest	Rest

A similar 3-week revision programme for Unifying Concepts in Chemistry is outlined below.

Day	Week 1	Week 2	Week 3
Mon	Topic 1 — Rates Allow about 30 minutes	Using past papers or other question sources, try a structured question on Topic 1 Mark it and list anything you do not understand Allow about 30 minutes	You have now revised all of Unit 6 and have attempted questions relating to each topic Make a list of your weaknesses and ask your teacher for help Reread all your summary notes at least twice Ask someone to help you
Tue	Topic 2(a) — K_c and (b) — K_p Allow about 30 minutes, followed by 10 minutes rereading yesterday's notes on Topic 1	Using past papers or other question sources, try a structured question on Topic 2(a) Mark it and list anything you do not understand Allow about 30 minutes	Using past papers or other question sources, try a relevant question that requires extended writing (essay-type question) from any of the topics Mark it and list anything you do not understand Allow about 30 minutes
Wed	Topic 3 — pH Allow about 30 minutes, followed by 10 minutes rereading yesterday's notes on Topic 2 and 5 minutes going over Topic 1	Using past papers or other question sources, try a structured question on Topic 2(b) Mark it and list anything you do not understand Allow about 30 minutes	Using past papers or other question sources, try a relevant question that requires extended writing (essay-type question) from any of the topics Mark it and list anything you do not understand Allow about 30 minutes
Thu	Topic 4 — Buffers Allow about 30 minutes, followed by 10 minutes rereading yesterday's notes on Topic 3, 5 minutes going over Topic 2 and, finally, 2 minutes on Topic 1	Using past papers or other question sources, try a structured question on Topic 3 Mark it and list anything you do not understand Allow about 30 minutes	Using past papers or other question sources, try a relevant question that requires extended writing (essay-type question) from any of the topics Mark it and list anything you do not understand Allow about 30 minutes

Day	Week 1	Week 2	Week 3
Fri	General revision of all four topics Allow about 30 minutes in total Topic 4 — 20 minutes Topic 3 — 5 minutes Topic 2 — 2 minutes Topic 1 — 1 minute	Using past papers or other question sources, try a structured question on Topic 4 Mark it and list anything you do not understand Allow about 30 minutes	Reread all your summary notes at least twice Concentrate on the weaknesses you identified on Monday (by now you should have talked to your teacher about them) Ask someone to test you
Sat	Rest	Rest	Rest
Sun	Reread all your summary notes at least twice	Using past papers or other question sources, try a structured question on each of the four topics Mark them and list anything you do not understand Allow about 45 minutes	Collect together about four structured questions and one extended answer question covering all four topics and try them under exam conditions Allow 1 hour 15 minutes Mark them and list anything you do not understand

This revision timetable may not suit you, in which case write one to meet your needs. It is only there to give you an idea of how one might work. The most important thing is that the grid at least enables you to see what you should be doing and when you should be doing it. Do not try to be too ambitious — *little and often is by far the best way*.

It would of course be sensible to put together a longer rolling programme to cover all your A2 subjects. At the very least it is highly likely that you will be taking both of these examinations at the same time and therefore it would be sensible to integrate both revision programmes. Try to work out a rolling programme that enables you to cover both over a 4-week period. Do *not* leave it too late. Start sooner rather than later.

Things you *must* do

- Leave yourself enough time to cover *all* the material.
- Make sure that you actually *have* all the material to hand (use this book as a basis).
- Identify weaknesses early in your preparation so that you have time to do something about them.
- Familiarise yourself with the terminology used in examination questions.

Things you *could* do to help you learn

- Copy selected portions of your notes.
- Write a precis of your notes, which includes all the key points.

- Write key points on postcards (carry them round with you for a quick revise during a coffee break!).
- Discuss a topic with a friend also studying the same course.
- Try to explain a topic to someone *not* on the course.
- Practise examination questions on the topic.

Approaching the unit test

Terms used in the unit test

You will be asked precise questions in the unit test, so you can save a lot of valuable time as well as ensuring you score as many marks as possible by knowing what is expected. Terms used most commonly are explained below.

Define
This requires a precise statement to explain a chemical term. It could involve specific amounts or conditions such as temperature and pressure.

Explain
This normally implies that a definition should be given, together with some relevant comment on the significance or context of the term(s) concerned, especially where two or more terms are included in the question. The amount of supplementary comment should be determined by the mark allocation.

State
This implies a concise answer with little or no supporting argument.

Describe
This requires you to state in words (but using diagrams where appropriate) the main points of the topic. It is often used with reference either to particular phenomena or to particular experiments. In the former instance, the term usually implies that the answer should include reference to observations associated with the phenomena. The amount of description should be determined by the mark allocation. You are not expected to explain the phenomena or experiments, but merely to describe them.

Deduce or predict
This means that you are not expected to produce the answer by recall but by making a logical connection between other pieces of information. Such information may be wholly given in the question or could depend on answers given in an earlier part of the question. 'Predict' also implies a concise answer, with no supporting statement required.

Outline
This implies brevity, i.e. restricting the answer to essential detail only.

Suggest
This is used in two contexts. It implies either that there is no unique answer or that

you are expected to apply your knowledge to a 'novel' situation that may not be formally in the specification.

Calculate

This is used when a numerical answer is required. In general, working should be shown.

Sketch

When this is applied to diagrams, it means that a simple, freehand drawing is acceptable. Nevertheless, care should be taken over proportions, and important details should be labelled clearly.

On the day

When you finally open the test paper, it can be quite a stressful moment and you need to be certain of your strategy.

The test paper for Trends and Patterns consists of structured questions (usually three or four) and free-response questions (usually one). The structured questions usually account for 37 or 38 marks and the free-response questions are worth 7 or 8 marks. The time allocation for this examination is 1 hour. The total number of marks on the paper is 45, of which 30 are *synoptic*. Synoptic means that the questions bring together principles and concepts from different areas of chemistry. Put simply, this means that the questions not only test the content of this module, but also relate to previous modules. This is likely to involve the sections on chemical bonding and the periodic table in Module 2811: Foundation Chemistry.

The test paper for Unifying Concepts in Chemistry consists of structured questions (usually three or four) and a free-response question (usually one). The structured questions usually account for 50 marks and the free-response question is worth 10 marks. The time allocation for this examination is 1 hour 15 minutes. The total number of marks on the paper is 60 marks. *All* of the marks in this paper are *synoptic*; they test the course content of this module and also relate to other modules such as 2811: Foundation Chemistry (mole calculations) and 2813: How Far, How Fast? (reaction rates and chemical equilibrium).

Time will be very tight. So:
- do *not* begin writing as soon as you open the paper
- scan *all* the questions before you begin to answer any
- identify those questions about which you feel most confident
- *read the question carefully* — if you are asked to explain, then explain, do *not* just describe
- take notice of the mark allocation and do not supply the examiner with all your knowledge of any topic if there is only 1 mark allocated — similarly, you have to come up with *four* ideas if 4 marks are allocated
- try to stick to the point in your answer — it is easy to stray into related areas that will not score marks and will use up valuable time
- try to answer *all* the questions

Structured questions

These are questions that may require a single-word answer, a short sentence or a response amounting to several sentences. The setter for the paper will have thought carefully about the amount of space required for the answer and the marks allocated, so the space provided usually gives a good indication of the amount of detail required.

Free-response questions

These questions enable you to demonstrate the depth and breadth of your knowledge as well as your ability to communicate chemical ideas in a concise way. These questions will often include marks for the quality of written communication. You are expected to use appropriate scientific terminology and to write in continuous prose, paying particular attention to spelling, punctuation and grammar.

Content
Guidance

This Content Guidance section is a student's guide to Component 01 of Modules 2815 and 2816. These modules build on a number of different areas of AS chemistry. The main topics in Module 2815 are:

- Lattice enthalpy and Born–Haber cycles
- Period 3
- Transition elements

Lattice enthalpy and Born–Haber cycles require an understanding of enthalpy change from Module 2813. The remaining topics centre around inorganic chemistry and require knowledge of chemical bonding and structure, the periodic table and the chemistry of group 2 and group 7 elements and their compounds. These topics were covered in Module 2811.

The main topics in Module 2816 are:

- How fast?
- How far?
- Acids, bases and buffers

The first of these (How fast?) requires an understanding of reaction rates from Module 2813. The remaining topics centre around equilibrium chemistry and build on the chemical equilibrium section of Module 2813.

Throughout this guide, essential prior knowledge is outlined and reference is made to the relevant AS modules.

Synoptic assessment

The Unit 2816 examination paper contains synoptic questions only. These questions relate the content of this module to knowledge and understanding acquired elsewhere in the course. You are expected to apply chemical principles from any part of the specification. The principles include:

- mole calculations
- writing balanced equations
- empirical and molecular formula calculations
- bonding and structure

This section includes all the relevant key facts required by the specification and explains the essential concepts.

Lattice enthalpy and Born–Haber cycles

Review of AS energetics

Chemical reactions are usually accompanied by a change in enthalpy (energy), normally in the form of heat energy. Reactions tend to be either **exothermic** or **endothermic**.

- If the reaction mixture loses energy to its surroundings, the reaction is exothermic and ΔH is negative.
- If the reaction mixture gains energy from its surroundings, the reaction is endothermic and ΔH is positive.

Standard enthalpy changes

All standard enthalpy changes are measured under standard conditions. The temperature and pressure at which measurements and/or calculations are carried out are standardised.

- Standard temperature = 298 K (25 °C)
- Standard pressure = 100 kPa (100 000 N m^{-2} = 10^5 Pa = 1 bar = 1 atmosphere)
- Standard temperature and pressure are often referred to as s.t.p.

Examinations often ask for definitions of enthalpy changes and it is advisable to learn these.

- **Standard enthalpy change of formation** is the enthalpy change when 1 mole of a substance is formed from its elements, in their natural state, under standard conditions of 298 K and 100 kPa.
- **Standard enthalpy change of combustion** is the enthalpy change when 1 mole of a substance is burnt completely, in an excess of oxygen, under standard conditions of 298 K and 100 kPa.
- **Average bond enthalpy** is the enthalpy change on breaking 1 mole of a covalent bond in a gaseous molecule under standard conditions of 298 K and 100 kPa.

You may also be expected to show your understanding by writing equations illustrating the standard enthalpy changes of formation and of combustion.

The standard enthalpy equation for the formation of ethane is given below:

1 mole of product must always be formed even if it means using fractions in the balanced equation

$$2C(s) + 3H_2(g) \longrightarrow 1C_2H_6(g)$$

It is essential to show all state symbols

The standard enthalpy equation for the combustion of ethane is given below:

1 mole of reactant must always be used even if it means using fractions in the balanced equation

$$1C_2H_6(g) + 3\tfrac{1}{2}O_2(g) \longrightarrow 2CO_2(g) + 3H_2O(l)$$

It is essential to show all state symbols

Average bond enthalpy

Bond (dissociation) enthalpy is the energy needed to break a bond. It is always endothermic ($+\Delta H$). The breaking of a bond, by homolytic fission, produces two neutral particles, for example:

$$H–Cl(g) \longrightarrow H(g) + Cl(g)$$

Bond enthalpies are the average (mean) values and take into account the chemical environment. In the water molecule, for instance, it is possible to break the two bonds successively. The energy involved differs for each bond.

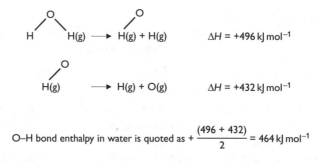

$O–H$ bond enthalpy in water is quoted as $+\dfrac{(496 + 432)}{2} = 464\,kJ\,mol^{-1}$

Activation energy

Activation energy is defined as the minimum energy required, in a collision between particles, for reaction to occur. In any chemical reaction, bonds are broken and new bonds are formed. Breaking bonds is an endothermic process requiring energy. This energy requirement influences the activation energy of a reaction.

Hess's law

Hess's law states that the enthalpy change for a reaction is the same irrespective of the route taken, provided that the initial and final conditions are the same.

Calculate the enthalpy change, ΔH_r, for the reaction:

$$2CO(g) + O_2(g) \longrightarrow 2CO_2(g)$$

The standard enthalpies of formation of $CO(g)$ and $CO_2(g)$ are $-110\,kJ\,mol^{-1}$ and $-394\,kJ\,mol^{-1}$ respectively.

Step 1

Write the equation for what you have been asked to calculate

$$2CO(g) + O_2(g) \xrightarrow{\Delta H_r} 2CO_2(g)$$

Step 2

Link both sides of the equation to the data given

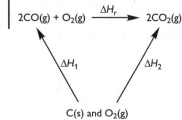

Step 3

Apply Hess's law: $\Delta H_r = \Delta H_2 - \Delta H_1$
$$\Delta H_1 = 2 \times (-110) = -220 \, \text{kJ mol}^{-1}$$
$$\Delta H_2 = 2 \times (-394) = -788 \, \text{kJ mol}^{-1}$$
$$\Delta H_r = -788 - (-220) \, \text{kJ mol}^{-1}$$
$$= -568 \, \text{kJ mol}^{-1}$$

The relationship between lattice enthalpy and Born–Haber cycles

Before moving on to lattice enthalpy, it may be helpful to review the required AS chemistry (see the guide to Module 2813).

Lattice enthalpy indicates the strength of the ionic bonds in an ionic lattice.

The **lattice enthalpy ($\Delta H_{latt}^{\ominus}$)** of an ionic compound is the enthalpy change that accompanies the formation of 1 mole of an ionic compound from its constituent gaseous ions. $\Delta H_{latt}^{\ominus}$ is exothermic. For example:

$$Na^+(g) + Cl^-(g) \longrightarrow Na^+Cl^-(s)$$

It is almost impossible to measure lattice enthalpy experimentally, so it is calculated using a **Born–Haber cycle**. A Born–Haber cycle is similar to a Hess's cycle, enabling calculation of enthalpy changes that cannot be measured directly.

The lattice enthalpy of sodium chloride can be calculated by considering the standard enthalpy of formation of NaCl(s). In order to form an ionic solid, both sodium and chlorine have to undergo a number of changes. These are outlined in the cycle below.

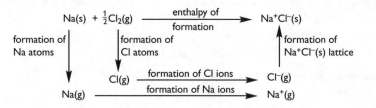

All the enthalpy changes in the cycle can be measured experimentally, except for the enthalpy of formation of the $Na^+Cl^-(s)$ lattice from its gaseous ions — the lattice enthalpy. However, because enthalpies for the other steps can be measured, the lattice enthalpy can be calculated. The cycle above has to be converted into a Born–Haber cycle, which is a combination of an enthalpy profile diagram and a Hess's cycle. The full Born–Haber cycle for sodium chloride is shown below.

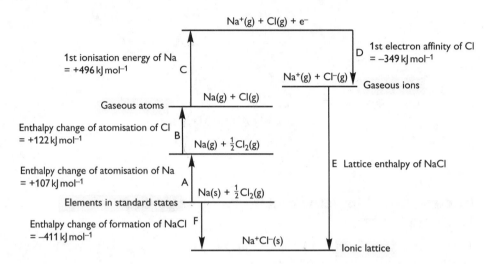

Route 1: **A + B + C + D + E**

Route 2: **F**

Using Hess's law: **A + B + C + D + E = F**

$$\Delta H^{\ominus}_{at} Na(g) + \Delta H^{\ominus}_{at} Cl(g) + \Delta H^{\ominus}_{IE} Na(g) + \Delta H^{\ominus}_{EA} Cl(g) + \mathbf{E} = \Delta H^{\ominus}_{f} Na^+Cl^-(s)$$
$$107 + 122 + 496 + (-349) + \mathbf{E} = -411$$

Hence, the lattice enthalpy of $Na^+Cl^-(s)$, **E** $= -787\ kJ\ mol^{-1}$

Definitions of enthalpy changes

Formation of an ionic compound

This is represented by step F in the Born–Haber cycle above.

The standard enthalpy change of formation, $\Delta H^{\ominus}_{f}$, is the enthalpy change that takes place when 1 mole of a substance is formed from its elements, in their natural state, under standard conditions. The standard enthalpy change of formation is usually exothermic for an ionic compound.

$$Na(s) + \tfrac{1}{2}Cl_2(g) \longrightarrow Na^+Cl^-(s) \quad \Delta H^{\ominus}_{f} = -411\ kJ\ mol^{-1}$$

Formation of gaseous atoms

This is represented by steps A and B in the Born–Haber cycle above.

The standard enthalpy change of atomisation, $\Delta H^{\ominus}_{at}$, of an element is the enthalpy change accompanying the formation of 1 mole of gaseous atoms from the element in its standard state. The standard enthalpy change of atomisation is always endothermic.

$$Na(s) \longrightarrow Na(g) \quad \Delta H^{\ominus}_{at} = +107\,kJ\,mol^{-1}$$
$$\tfrac{1}{2}Cl_2(g) \longrightarrow Cl(g) \quad \Delta H^{\ominus}_{at} = +122\,kJ\,mol^{-1}$$

For gaseous molecules, this enthalpy change can be determined from the **bond dissociation enthalpy**. This is the enthalpy change required to break and separate 1 mole of bonds so that the resulting gaseous atoms exert no forces on each other.

$$Cl–Cl(g) \longrightarrow 2Cl(g)\,\Delta H^{\ominus}_{BDE} = +244\,kJ\,mol^{-1}$$
$$\tfrac{1}{2}Cl–Cl(g) \longrightarrow Cl(g)\,\Delta H^{\ominus}_{at} = +122\,kJ\,mol^{-1}$$

Formation of positive ions

This is represented by step C in the Born–Haber cycle on page 18.

The first ionisation energy, $\Delta H^{\ominus}_{IE}$, of an element is the enthalpy change that accompanies the removal of one electron from each atom in 1 mole of gaseous atoms to form 1 mole of gaseous ions of charge +1. The first ionisation energy is always endothermic.

$$Na(g) \longrightarrow Na^+(g) + e^- \quad \Delta H^{\ominus}_{IE} = +496\,kJ\,mol^{-1}$$

Formation of negative ions

This is represented by step D in the Born–Haber cycle on page 18.

The first electron affinity, $\Delta H^{\ominus}_{EA}$, of an element is the enthalpy change that accompanies the addition of one electron to each atom in 1 mole of gaseous atoms to form 1 mole of gaseous ions of charge –1. The first electron affinity is usually exothermic.

$$Cl(g) + e^- \longrightarrow Cl^-(g) \quad \Delta H^{\ominus}_{EA} = -349\,kJ\,mol^{-1}$$

Lattice enthalpy calculations

The lattice enthalpy for magnesium chloride and for magnesium oxide can be calculated using the following data.

	Standard enthalpy change	Equation	$\Delta H/kJ\,mol^{-1}$
A	Formation of $MgCl_2(s)$	$Mg(s) + Cl_2(g) \longrightarrow MgCl_2(s)$	−641
B	Formation of MgO(s)	$Mg(s) + \tfrac{1}{2}O_2(g) \longrightarrow MgO(s)$	−602
C	Atomisation of magnesium	$Mg(s) \longrightarrow Mg(g)$	+148
D	Atomisation of chlorine	$\tfrac{1}{2}Cl_2(g) \longrightarrow Cl(g)$	+122
E	Atomisation of oxygen	$\tfrac{1}{2}O_2(g) \longrightarrow O(g)$	+249
F	First ionisation energy of Mg	$Mg(g) \longrightarrow Mg^+(g) + 1e^-$	+738
G	Second ionisation energy of Mg	$Mg^+(g) \longrightarrow Mg^{2+}(g) + 1e^-$	+1451
H	First electron affinity of Cl	$Cl(g) + 1e^- \longrightarrow Cl^-(g)$	−349
I	First electron affinity of O	$O(g) + 1e^- \longrightarrow O^-(g)$	−141
J	Second electron affinity of O	$O^-(g) + 1e^- \longrightarrow O^{2-}(g)$	+798

The Born–Haber cycle for magnesium chloride is shown below.

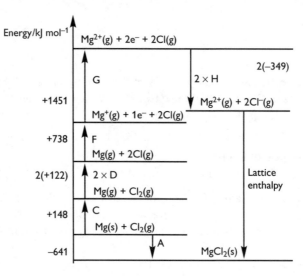

Applying Hess's law to the Born–Haber cycle gives:

A = C + 2D + F + G + 2H + lattice enthalpy

lattice enthalpy = A – C – 2D – F – G – 2H

The lattice enthalpy of magnesium chloride is:

= –641 – 148 – 244 – 738 – 1451 – (–698)

= –2524 kJ mol⁻¹

The Born–Haber cycle for magnesium oxide is very similar. However, in order to form the oxide ion, O^{2-}, the oxygen atom has to gain two electrons and consequently has two electron affinities. The first electron affinity is exothermic; the second electron affinity is endothermic.

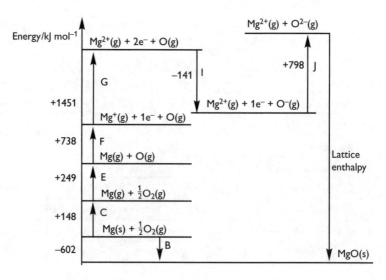

Apply Hess's law to the cycle above to show that the lattice enthalpy of magnesium oxide is $-3845\,\text{kJ}\,\text{mol}^{-1}$.

Factors affecting the size of lattice enthalpies

The strength of an ionic lattice and the value of its lattice enthalpy depend upon ionic radii and ionic charges.

Effect of ionic size

Compound	Lattice enthalpy/ kJ mol^{-1}	Ions	Effect of ionic radius of halide ion
NaCl	−787		As the ionic radius increases: • the charge density decreases • the attraction between ions decreases • the lattice enthalpy becomes less negative
NaBr	−751		
NaI	−705		

Note that lattice enthalpy has a negative value. When describing lattice enthalpies, you should use the term *'becomes less/more negative'* rather than *'becomes bigger/ smaller'*.

Effect of ionic charge

The strongest ionic lattices contain small, highly charged ions.

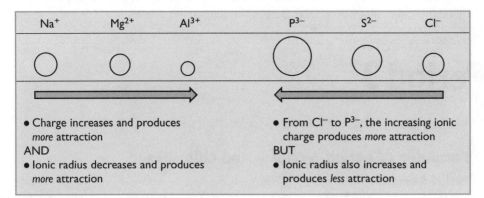

• Charge increases and produces *more* attraction
AND
• Ionic radius decreases and produces *more* attraction

• From Cl⁻ to P³⁻, the increasing ionic charge produces *more* attraction
BUT
• Ionic radius also increases and produces *less* attraction

Limitations of lattice enthalpies

Theoretical lattice enthalpies can be calculated by considering each ion as a perfect sphere. Any difference between this theoretical lattice enthalpy and lattice enthalpy calculated using a Born–Haber cycle indicates a degree of covalent bonding caused by polarisation. Polarisation is greatest between a small, densely charged cation and a large anion. This is most apparent in group 2 carbonates.

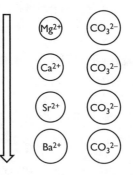

As the ionic radius increases:
- the charge density decreases and the attraction between ions decreases. This causes a decrease in lattice enthalpy and should result in a decrease in thermal stability. This suggests $MgCO_3$ should be the more stable.
- the amount of polarisation decreases and the degree of covalent bonding decreases. As the degree of covalency decreases, the strength of the ionic lattic should increase and result in an increase in thermal stability. This suggests that $BaCO_3$ should be the more stable.

However, $MgCO_3$ decomposes at $350\,°C$ while $BaCO_3$ decomposes at a much higher temperature of $1450\,°C$, showing that the degree of polarisation is the more significant factor.

The decomposition temperature of MgO is extremely high because each molecule consists of two small, highly charged ions. Therefore, it has a high lattice enthalpy. Both ions are of similar size so there is little or no polarisation. This makes MgO so thermally stable that it is used as a refractory lining in furnaces.

Period 3

You should be familiar with the AS topics listed on pages 15–17 of this book.

Formulae of period 3 oxides and chlorides

Period 3 oxides

Across period 3, the formulae of oxides show a regular pattern depending upon the number of electrons in the outer shell.

The **oxidation state** of an element indicates the number of electrons involved in bonding. In oxides, the highest oxidation state of an element is usually the group number. It represents the number of electrons of the element involved in bonding to oxygen.

Element	Formula of oxide	Oxidation state	
Na	Na_2O	+1	basic
Mg	MgO	+2	basic
Al	Al_2O_3	+3	amphoteric
Si	SiO_2	+4	acidic
P	P_4O_{10}	+5	
S	SO_3	+6	↓

The number of oxygen atoms combined with one atom of the element increases steadily across period 3.

For each element in the period, there is an increase of 0.5 mole of O per mole of element

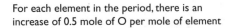

$Na_1O_{0.5}$ Mg_1O_1 $Al_1O_{1.5}$ Si_1O_2 $P_1O_{2.5}$ S_1O_3

Period 3 chlorides

Across period 3, the formulae of chlorides show a regular pattern depending upon the number of electrons in the outer shell. In the chlorides, the highest oxidation state of an element is usually the group number. It represents the number of electrons of the element involved in bonding to chlorine.

Element	Formula of chloride	Oxidation state	
Na	NaCl	+1	neutral
Mg	$MgCl_2$	+2	6.5
Al	Al_2Cl_6	+3	acidic
Si	$SiCl_4$	+4	
P	PCl_3	+5	↓
	PCl_5		

The number of chlorine atoms combined with one atom of the element increases steadily across period 3.

For each element in the period, there is an increase of 1 mole of Cl per mole of element

NaCl $MgCl_2$ Al_2Cl_6 $SiCl_4$ PCl_5

Preparation of oxides and chlorides from the elements

Preparation of oxides

Oxides of the period 3 elements Na to Cl can be prepared by heating the element in oxygen. This is a **redox reaction**; the period 3 element is oxidised and oxygen is reduced.

Metal oxides

Element	Equation	Oxide	Flame colour
Na	$4Na(s) + O_2(g) \longrightarrow 2Na_2O(s)$	White solid	Yellow
Mg	$2Mg(s) + O_2(g) \longrightarrow 2MgO\ (s)$	White solid	White
Al	$4Al(s) + 3O_2(g) \longrightarrow 2Al_2O_3(s)$	White solid	White

Na_2O and MgO are **ionic** compounds, but Al_2O_3 has bonding *intermediate* between ionic and covalent. This can be explained by the polarisation of the oxide ion by the small, highly charged Al^{3+} ion, which results in an increase in covalent character.

Non-metal oxides

Element	Equation	Oxide	Flame colour
P	$4P(s) + 5O_2(g) \longrightarrow P_4O_{10}(s)$	White solid	White
S	$S(s) + O_2(g) \longrightarrow SO_2(g)$	Colourless gas	Blue

SO_2 reacts further with oxygen in the presence of a vanadium pentoxide catalyst to form sulphur trioxide, which is a colourless liquid:

$$2SO_2(g) + O_2(g) \longrightarrow 2SO_3(l)$$

P_4O_{10}, SO_2 and SO_3 are **covalent** compounds.

Preparation of chlorides

Chlorides of period 3 can be prepared by heating the elements in chlorine. This is a **redox reaction**; the period 3 element is oxidised and chlorine is reduced.

Ionic chlorides

Element	Equation	Chloride
Na	$2Na(s) + Cl_2(g) \longrightarrow 2NaCl(s)$	White solid
Mg	$Mg(s) + Cl_2(g) \longrightarrow MgCl_2(s)$	White solid

Sodium chloride and magnesium chloride are ionic compounds.

Covalent chlorides

Element	Equation	Chloride	Flame colour
Al	$2Al(s) + 3Cl_2(g) \longrightarrow Al_2Cl_6(s)$	White solid	—
Si	$Si(s) + 2Cl_2(g) \longrightarrow SiCl_4(l)$	Colourless liquid	—
P	$2P(s) + 3Cl_2(g) \longrightarrow 2PCl_3(l)$	Colourless liquid	Pale green

PCl$_3$ reacts further under ice-cold conditions to produce the white solid PCl$_5$:

PCl$_3$(l) + Cl$_2$(l) $\longrightarrow$ PCl$_5$(s)

Ionic and covalent nature of period 3 oxides and chlorides

This can be explained by the trends in periodicity, which are covered in Module 2811. It would be sensible to revise the relevant topics. The key facts are outlined in the tables below.

Oxide	Boiling point/°C	Structure	Bonding	Forces
Na$_2$O	1275	Giant lattice	Ionic	Strong forces between ions
MgO	2827	Giant lattice	Ionic	Strong forces between ions
Al$_2$O$_3$	2017	Giant lattice	Intermediate	Strong forces between ions
SiO$_2$	1607		Covalent	Strong forces between atoms
P$_4$O$_{10}$	580	Simple molecule	Covalent	Weak intermolecular forces
SO$_3$	33	Simple molecule	Covalent	Weak intermolecular forces

Chloride	Boiling point/°C	Structure	Bonding	Forces
NaCl	1413	Giant lattice	Ionic	Strong forces between ions
MgCl$_2$	1412	Giant lattice	Ionic	Strong forces between ions
Al$_2$Cl$_6$	178	Simple molecule	Covalent	Weak intermolecular forces
SiCl$_4$	58	Simple molecule	Covalent	Weak intermolecular forces
PCl$_5$	56	Simple molecule	Covalent	Weak intermolecular forces

Giant structures and boiling point

Giant structures have high boiling points and require a large amount of energy to break the strong forces between their particles.

The particles making up a giant lattice can be ionic, covalent or intermediate:
- Ionic — Na$_2$O, MgO, NaCl and MgCl$_2$. The strong forces are electrostatic attractions acting between positive and negative ions.
- Covalent — SiO$_2$. The strong forces are shared pairs of electrons acting between the atoms (covalent bonds).
- Intermediate — Al$_2$O$_3$. The strong forces act between particles throughout the lattice.

Simple molecular structures and boiling point

Simple molecular structures have low boiling points because only a small amount of energy is required to break the weak van der Waals forces acting between molecules.

Action of water on period 3 oxides

Sodium and magnesium oxides

Metal oxides form alkaline solutions in water:

$$Na_2O(s) + 2H_2O(l) \longrightarrow 2NaOH(aq) \quad pH = 14$$

The hydroxides dissociate in water, releasing OH^- ions into solution. For example:

$$NaOH(aq) \longrightarrow Na^+(aq) + OH^-(aq)$$

Although MgO reacts with water, the $Mg(OH)_2$ formed is only slightly soluble in water and forms a weakly alkaline solution.

Aluminium and silicon oxides

Al_2O_3 and SiO_2 have very strong lattices, which cannot be broken down by water. Consequently, these compounds are insoluble in water.

Non-metal oxides

Non-metal oxides form acidic solutions in water.

$$P_4O_{10}(s) + 6H_2O(l) \longrightarrow 4H_3PO_4(aq)$$
$$\text{Phosphoric acid}$$

$$SO_2(g) + H_2O(l) \longrightarrow H_2SO_3(aq)$$
$$\text{Sulphurous acid}$$

$$SO_3(l) + H_2O(l) \longrightarrow H_2SO_4(aq)$$
$$\text{Sulphuric acid}$$

Each acid dissociates to some degree in water, releasing H^+ ions into solution. For example:

$$H_2SO_4(aq) \longrightarrow H^+(aq) + HSO_4^-(aq)$$

Tip An important general rule is that *metal oxides* are *basic* and *non-metal oxides* are *acidic*.

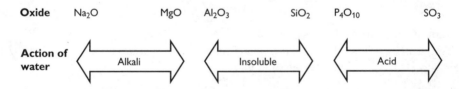

Action of water on period 3 chlorides

Metal chlorides

The ionic chlorides dissolve in water to form neutral or very weakly acidic solutions. For example:

$$NaCl(s) + aq \longrightarrow Na^+(aq) + Cl^-(aq) \qquad pH = 7$$
$$MgCl_2(s) + aq \longrightarrow Mg^{2+}(aq) + 2Cl^-(aq) \quad pH = 6$$

Non-metal chlorides

Non-metal chlorides are covalent and are *vigorously* hydrolysed by water. Strong acid solutions containing hydrochloric acid are formed.

$$Al_2Cl_6(s) + 6H_2O(l) \longrightarrow 2Al(OH)_3(s) + 6HCl(aq)$$
$$SiCl_4(l) + 2H_2O(l) \longrightarrow SiO_2(s) + 4HCl(aq)$$
$$PCl_5(s) + 4H_2O(l) \longrightarrow H_3PO_4(aq) + 5HCl(aq)$$

These reactions are exothermic and the HCl released can produce misty white fumes.

Tip *Ionic chlorides* form *neutral* solutions and *covalent chlorides* form *acidic* solutions in water.

Transition elements

A transition element is defined as a *d*-block element that forms one or more stable ions with partly filled *d*-orbitals.

The fourth period runs from K to Kr.

s-block		d-block										p-block					
K	Ca	Sc	Ti	V	Cr	Mn	Fe	Co	Ni	Cu	Zn	Ga	Ge	As	Se	Br	Kr

Electronic configurations of *d*-block elements

The 4*s* sub-shell is at a lower energy level than the 3*d* sub-shell and therefore the 4*s* sub-shell fills before the 3*d* sub-shell. The orbitals in the 3*d* sub-shell are first occupied singly, preventing any repulsion caused by pairing.

Filling the 4s and 3d sub-shells

		4s	3d				
Sc	[Ar]$3d^14s^2$	↑↓	↑				
Ti	[Ar]$3d^24s^2$	↑↓	↑	↑			
V	[Ar]$3d^34s^2$	↑↓	↑	↑	↑		
Cr*	[Ar]$3d^54s^1$	↑	↑	↑	↑	↑	↑
Mn	[Ar]$3d^54s^2$	↑↓	↑	↑	↑	↑	↑
Fe^{2+}	[Ar]$3d^64s^2$	↑↓	↑↓	↑	↑	↑	↑
Co	[Ar]$3d^74s^2$	↑↓	↑↓	↑↓	↑	↑	↑
Ni	[Ar]$3d^84s^2$	↑↓	↑↓	↑↓	↑↓	↑	↑
Cu**	[Ar]$3d^{10}4s^1$	↑	↑↓	↑↓	↑↓	↑↓	↑↓
Zn	[Ar]$3d^{10}4s^2$	↑↓	↑↓	↑↓	↑↓	↑↓	↑↓

*Chromium has one electron in each orbital of the 4*s* and 3*d* sub-shells, giving the configuration [Ar]$3d^54s^1$, which is more stable than [Ar]$3d^44s^2$.

**Copper has a full 3*d* sub-shell, giving the configuration [Ar]$3d^{10}4s^1$, which is more stable than [Ar]$3d^94s^2$.

The majority of transition elements form ions in more than one oxidation state. When transition elements form ions, they do so by losing electrons from the $4s$ orbitals before the $3d$ orbitals. Sc and Zn each form ions in one oxidation state only: Sc^{3+} and Zn^{2+} respectively. The electronic configurations of these ions are $[Ar]3d^0$ and $[Ar]3d^{10}$ respectively. Neither fits the definition of a transition element.

Typical properties

- The transition elements are all metals and therefore they are good conductors of heat and electricity.
- They are denser than other metals. They have smaller atoms than the metals in groups 1 and 2, so the atoms are able to pack together more closely, hence increasing the density.
- They have higher melting and boiling points than other metals. This can also be explained by considering the size of their atoms. Within the metallic lattice, ions are smaller than those of the s-block metals, which results in greater 'free-electron density' and hence a stronger metallic bond.
- They have moderate to low reactivity. Unlike the s-block metals, they do not react with cold water. Many transition metals react with dilute acids, although some, for instance gold, silver and platinum, are very unreactive.
- They have compounds with two or more oxidation states. This is primarily due to the fact that successive ionisation energies of transition metals increase only gradually.
- They have at least one oxidation state that is coloured, so their compounds and ions are coloured. The colours are often distinctive and can be used as a means of identification.
- The ions of transition elements form complex ions with ligands.
- Many transition elements can act as catalysts. For example, iron is used in the Haber process.

Simple precipitation reactions

A precipitation reaction takes place between an aqueous alkali and an aqueous solution of a metal(II) or metal(III) cation. This results in formation of a precipitate of the metal hydroxide, which often has a characteristic colour. A suitable aqueous alkali is NaOH(aq). The colour of the precipitate can be used as a means of identification.

Some precipitation reactions can be represented as follows:

$$Cu^{2+}(aq) + 2OH^-(aq) \longrightarrow Cu(OH)_2(s)$$
Pale blue precipitate

$$Fe^{2+}(aq) + 2OH^-(aq) \longrightarrow Fe(OH)_2(s)$$
Pale green gelatinous precipitate

$$Fe^{3+}(aq) + 3OH^-(aq) \longrightarrow Fe(OH)_3(s)$$
Orange-brown gelatinous precipitate

$Fe(OH)_2(s)$ is slowly oxidised to $Fe(OH)_3(s)$. Therefore, on standing, the pale green precipitate changes to an orange-brown precipitate.

Transition metal complexes

Ligands and complex ions

Transition metal ions are small and densely charged. They strongly attract electron-rich species, called ligands, forming complex ions.

A **ligand** is defined as a molecule or ion that bonds to a metal ion by forming a coordinate (dative covalent) bond. It does this by donating a lone pair of electrons into a vacant d-orbital.

Common ligands include: $H_2O:$, $:Cl^-$, $:NH_3$ and $:CN^-$, all of which have at least one lone pair of electrons.

A **complex ion** is defined as a central metal ion surrounded by ligands.

Some complex ions of Cu^{2+} are:

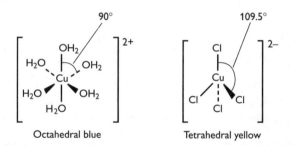

Octahedral blue   Tetrahedral yellow

In $[Cu(H_2O)_6]^{2+}$, the six electron pairs surrounding the central Cu^{2+} ion repel one another so that they are as far apart as possible. The complex ion has an octahedral shape, so all the bond angles are 90°.

In $[CuCl_4]^{2-}$, the four electron pairs surrounding the central Cu^{2+} ion repel one another as far apart as possible and the complex ion has a tetrahedral shape with bond angles of 109°28′.

Coordination number

The **coordination number** is defined as the total number of coordinate bonds between the ligands and the central transition metal ion in a complex ion.

Complex ions with ligands such as H_2O and NH_3 are usually 6-coordinate and octahedral in shape.

Complex ions with Cl^- ligands are usually 4-coordinate and tetrahedral in shape.

Ligand substitution in complex ions

A ligand substitution reaction takes place when a ligand in a complex ion is replaced by another ligand.

Exchange of H_2O and NH_3 ligands

Water and ammonia ligands have *similar* sizes so, on exchange, the coordination number does not change.

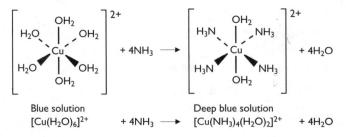

$$[Cu(H_2O)_6]^{2+} + 4NH_3 \longrightarrow [Cu(NH_3)_4(H_2O)_2]^{2+} + 4H_2O$$

Exchange of H_2O and Cl^- ligands

Water molecules and chloride ions have *different* sizes so, on exchange, the coordination number often changes.

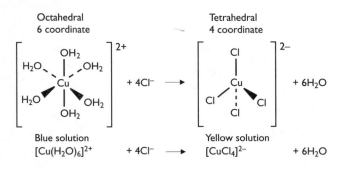

$$[Cu(H_2O)_6]^{2+} + 4Cl^- \longrightarrow [CuCl_4]^{2-} + 6H_2O$$

The ligand substitution reaction between H_2O and the thiocyanate ion, SCN^-, can be used to identify the presence of the Fe^{3+} ion. It is a sensitive test which can be used to detect very low concentrations.

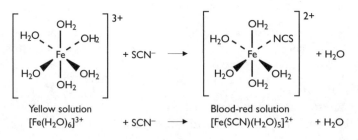

$$[Fe(H_2O)_6]^{3+} + SCN^- \longrightarrow [Fe(SCN)(H_2O)_5]^{2+} + H_2O$$

Colour in transition metal complexes

Colour of complex ions

The colour of a transition metal complex ion results from movement of electrons between the orbitals of a partly filled d sub-shell. It follows that only those ions that have a partially filled d sub-shell are coloured.

Cu²⁺ and Cu⁺

- Cu^{2+} has the electronic configuration $[Ar]3d^9$, which has partly filled d-orbitals. Therefore, electrons can absorb light energy and produce the corresponding complementary colour.
- Cu^+ has the electronic configuration $[Ar]3d^{10}$, which has a completely full set of d-orbitals, preventing the electrons from absorbing light energy. Hence, the Cu^+ ion is not coloured.

Colorimetry

A colorimeter measures the amount of light absorbed by a coloured solution. The formula of a complex ion can be determined from the intensity of light absorbed by the colorimeter. The colour of a transition metal ion can change if one or more of the ligands are changed. By making up a range of mixtures using transition metal and ligand solutions of *equal concentration*, we can use this colour change to find the ratio of the transition metal ion to the new ligand.

A basic colorimeter measures absorbance of solutions by passing a narrow beam of light through the sample.

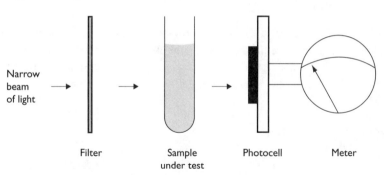

| Narrow beam of light | Filter | Sample under test | Photocell | Meter |

Each mixture has a difference absorbance. The maximum absorbance indicates the proportion of ligand present in the complex ion and tells us the ratio of transition metal ion to new ligand.

Finding the formula of a complex ion using colorimetry

A common example is to start with solutions of Fe^{3+} and SCN^- of equal concentrations, and to prepare mixtures as shown in the table below. The total volume of each mixture is $10\,cm^3$.

Mixture	1	2	3	4	5	6	7	8	9	10	11
Volume 0.1 mol dm⁻³ Fe^{3+}(aq)/cm³	10	9	8	7	6	5	4	3	2	1	0
Volume 0.1 mol dm⁻³ SCN^- (aq)/cm³	0	1	2	3	4	5	6	7	8	9	10

The absorbance for each mixture is measured and plotted as shown below:

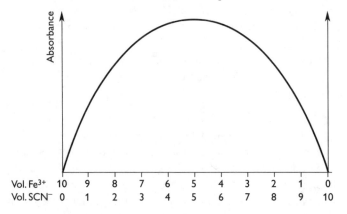

| Vol. Fe^{3+} | 10 | 9 | 8 | 7 | 6 | 5 | 4 | 3 | 2 | 1 | 0 |
| Vol. SCN^- | 0 | 1 | 2 | 3 | 4 | 5 | 6 | 7 | 8 | 9 | 10 |

The graph is used to estimate the ratio of Fe^{3+}:SCN^- at maximum absorbance. This is 5:5 and hence the ratio of transition metal ion to new ligand is 1:1. Therefore, one of the H_2O ligands has been replaced by one SCN^- ion. The formula of the new complex ion is $Fe(H_2O)_5(SCN)^{2+}$.

Predicting the colour of a complex ion from its ultraviolet/visible spectrum

Transition metal ions have partly filled d-orbitals. The d-electrons can absorb visible light and are able to move from one d-orbital to another. The result of the absorption of visible light is that the ions appear to be coloured. Visible light has a wavelength, λ, in the region 400–650 nm.

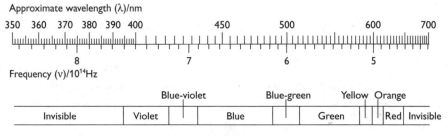

The blue end of the spectrum is short wavelength and the red end is long wavelength.

The table below gives approximate wavelength values for colours absorbed and some examples of colours we would see.

λ/nm	400	450	500	550	600	650
Absorbed colour	Violet	Blue	Blue-green	Green	Yellow-orange	Red
Observed colour	Yellow		Red		Violet	Blue

It should be possible to predict the colour of a complex by analysis of its visible spectrum.

Sample A:

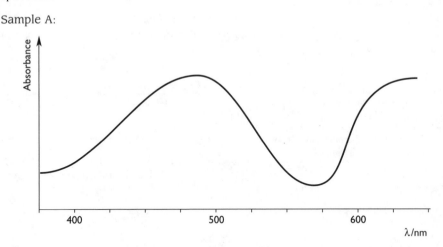

Sample A absorbs visible light in the region 400–550 nm and around 650 nm. The colours of light absorbed are:
- 400–550 nm — violet, blue, blue-green and green
- 650 nm — red

The wavelengths of light *not* absorbed lie between 550 and 650 nm. Therefore, sample A appears to have a yellow-orange colour.

Sample B:

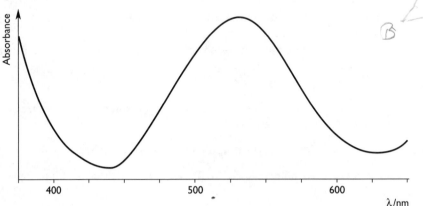

Sample B absorbs visible light in the region 480–580 nm. The colours of light absorbed are:
- 480–580 nm — blue-green, green

The wavelengths of light *not* absorbed are at each end of the visible spectrum, i.e. blue and red. Therefore, sample B appears to have a blue-red or purple colour.

Redox reactions

Oxidation number

The oxidation number is a convenient way of identifying quickly whether or not a substance has undergone either oxidation or reduction. In order to work out the oxidation number, you must learn a few simple rules.

	Rule	Example
1	All elements in their natural state have an oxidation number of zero	H_2: oxidation number of H is 0
2	The oxidation numbers in any molecule always add up to zero	H_2O: sum of oxidation numbers in water is 0
3	The oxidation numbers of any ion always add up to the charge on the ion	SO_4^{2-}: sum of oxidation numbers is −2
4	Elements in groups 1, 2 and 3 have oxidation numbers of +1, +2 and +3 respectively	NaCl: Na is +1 $MgCl_2$: Mg is +2 $AlCl_3$: Al is +3
5	Fluorine is always −1	HF: F is −1
6	Hydrogen is usually +1	H_2O: H is +1
7	Oxygen is usually −2	H_2O: O is −2
8	Transition elements have no fixed oxidation number	Variable oxidation numbers (e.g. Fe: +2, +3)

In **redox** reactions involving transition metal ions, the metal ions change their oxidation state by gaining or losing electrons.

- Movement of electrons — **o**xidation **is** the **l**oss of electrons; **r**eduction **is** the **g**ain of electrons (OILRIG).
- Change in oxidation state/number — oxidation is an increase in oxidation number; reduction is a decrease.

The iron(II)–manganate(VII) reaction

The most common redox reaction involving transition elements you will meet is the reaction between Fe^{2+}(aq) and MnO_4^-(aq).

Step 1: *Write an ionic half-equation for each transition metal.*

In this reaction, Fe^{2+}(aq) changes to Fe^{3+}(aq). This can be written as a half-equation:

$$Fe^{2+} \longrightarrow Fe^{3+} + 1e^- \qquad \text{(equation 1)}$$

Like any balanced equation, both the symbols and the charges have to balance. Fe^{2+} loses one electron when it is **oxidised** to Fe^{3+}. If Fe^{2+} is oxidised, it follows that MnO_4^-(aq) must be reduced. It is in fact reduced to Mn^{2+}. The first step in constructing a half-equation for this reduction is to recognise the change in oxidation state of the Mn. Using the table above:

- Rule 3: the oxidation numbers of any ion always add up to the charge on the ion.
- Rule 7: oxygen is usually −2.

It follows that for Mn^{2+}, the oxidation state of the Mn is +2. For MnO_4^-:

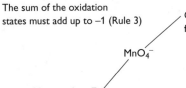

The sum of the oxidation states must add up to –1 (Rule 3)

Oxygen = –2 (Rule 7) and since there are four oxygen atoms, the total = –8

MnO_4^-

Mn must be +7, such that +7 – 8 = –1

Mn gains $5e^-$ and changes from +7 to +2:

$$MnO_4^- + 5e^- \longrightarrow Mn^{2+}$$

Clearly this half-equation is *not* balanced. Each O in the MnO_4^- forms a water molecule. This reaction will not take place unless the MnO_4^- is acidified. Since there are four oxygen atoms in MnO_4^-, four water molecules will be formed, requiring eight H^+ ions.

$$MnO_4^- + 8H^+ + 5e^- \longrightarrow Mn^{2+} + 4H_2O \qquad \text{(equation 2)}$$

Each half-equation is now balanced:

$$Fe^{2+} \longrightarrow Fe^{3+} + 1e^- \qquad \text{(equation 1)}$$
$$MnO_4^- + 8H^+ + 5e^- \longrightarrow Mn^{2+} + 4H_2O \qquad \text{(equation 2)}$$

Step 2: *Rewrite the half-equations so that the number of electrons in both is the same.*

In this case, we need to multiply equation 1 by 5, giving:

$$5Fe^{2+} \longrightarrow 5Fe^{3+} + 5e^-$$

Equation 2 remains the same:

$$MnO_4^- + 8H^+ + 5e^- \longrightarrow Mn^{2+} + 4H_2O$$

Step 3: *Add the last two half-equations together to cancel out the electrons.*

So the overall reaction equation is:

$$5Fe^{2+} + MnO_4^- + 8H^+ \longrightarrow 5Fe^{3+} + Mn^{2+} + 4H_2O$$

You can double check that the final equation is correct by making sure the charges on each side balance.

Redox titrations

Transition metal ions are often coloured and the colour changes that occur when they react can be used to show when a titration has reached its end point. The reaction of Fe^{2+} with MnO_4^- is a good example. MnO_4^- is purple while Mn^{2+} is very pale pink or almost colourless. When purple MnO_4^- is added from a burette into acidified Fe^{2+}, it immediately turns pale pink or colourless as the MnO_4^- reacts with the acidified Fe^{2+}. When all of the Fe^{2+} has reacted, the purple colour of further MnO_4^- added remains. The end point of this titration is when a faint permanent pink colour is seen.

The reaction between Fe^{2+} and MnO_4^- is often tested in the context of a titration calculation.

Example

Five iron tablets with a combined mass of 0.900 g were dissolved in acid and made up to 100 cm^3 of solution. In a titration, 10.0 cm^3 of this solution reacted exactly with 10.4 cm^3 of 0.0100 mol dm^{-3} potassium manganate(VII). What is the percentage by mass of iron in the tablets?

Step 1: *Write the balanced equation.*

$$5Fe^{2+}(aq) + MnO_4^-(aq) + 8H^+(aq) \longrightarrow 5Fe^{3+}(aq) + Mn^{2+}(aq) + 4H_2O(l)$$

Use the balanced equation to obtain the mole ratio of Fe^{2+} to MnO_4^-, which is 5:1.

Calculate the number of moles of MnO_4^- by using the concentration, c, and the reacting volume, v, of $KMnO_4$.

From the titration results, the amount of $KMnO_4$ can be calculated:

$$\text{Amount of } KMnO_4 = c \times \frac{v}{1000}$$

$$= 0.0100 \times \frac{10.4}{1000} = 1.04 \times 10^{-4} \text{ mol}$$

From the mole ratio, the amount of Fe^{2+} can be determined.

The Fe^{2+} to MnO_4 ratio is 5:1. The amount of $KMnO_4$ is 1.04×10^{-4} mol.

Mol Fe^{2+} reacting with 1.04×10^{-4} mol $MnO_4^- = 5 \times 1.04 \times 10^{-4}$

Therefore, amount of Fe^{2+} that reacted $= 5.20 \times 10^{-4}$ mol

Step 2: *Find the amount of Fe^{2+} in the solution prepared from the tablets.*

10.0 cm^3 of Fe^{2+}(aq) contains 5.20×10^{-4} mol Fe^{2+}(aq)

100 cm^3 solution of iron tablets contains $10 \times (5.20 \times 10^{-4}) = 5.20 \times 10^{-3}$ mol Fe^{2+}

Step 3: *Find the percentage of Fe^{2+} in the tablets (A_r: Fe, 55.8).*

5.20×10^{-3} mol Fe^{2+} has a mass of $5.20 \times 10^{-3} \times 55.8 = 0.290$ g

Therefore, % of Fe^{2+} in tablets $= \dfrac{\text{mass of } Fe^{2+}}{\text{mass of tablets}} \times 100$

$$= \frac{0.290}{0.900} \times 100 = 32.2\%$$

Task Here are some common half-equations:

(1) $MnO_4^- + 8H^+ + 5e^- \longrightarrow Mn^{2+} + 4H_2O$
(2) $Cr_2O_7^{2-} + 14H^+ + 6e^- \longrightarrow 2Cr^{3+} + 7H_2O$
(3) $H_2O_2 + 2H^+ + 2e^- \longrightarrow 2H_2O$

Each of the above reactions oxidises Fe^{2+} to Fe^{3+}. Construct a balanced equation for each reaction.

(Answers are on page 59.)

How fast?

This topic builds on your understanding of the reaction rate chemistry covered at AS. It involves measuring and calculating reaction rates using rate equations.

Overview of required AS chemistry

Experimental observations show that the rate of a reaction is influenced by temperature, concentration and the use of a catalyst.

The collision theory of reactivity helps to provide explanations for these observations. A reaction cannot take place unless a collision occurs between the reacting particles. Increasing temperature or concentration increases the chance of a collision occurring. However, not all collisions result in reaction. The energy of a collision between reacting particles must exceed the minimum energy required for the reaction to occur. This minimum energy is known as the activation energy, E_a. Increasing the temperature increases the number of collisions with energy that exceeds the activation energy. Catalysts reduce the value of the activation energy.

Boltzmann distribution of molecular energies

The graph below shows a typical distribution of energies at constant temperature.

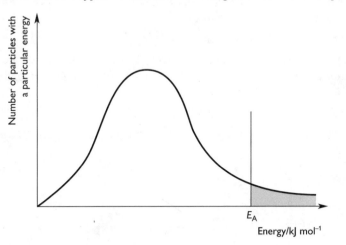

- The area under the curve represents the total number of particles.
- The shaded area represents the number of particles with energy greater than or equal to the activation energy ($E \geqslant E_a$). It shows the number of particles with sufficient energy to react.

The effect of concentration, temperature and use of a catalyst

Concentration

Increasing the concentration increases the chance of a collision. The more collisions there are, the faster the reaction will be.

For a gaseous reaction, increasing pressure has the same effect as increasing concentration. When gases react, they react faster at high pressure because there is an increased chance of a collision.

Temperature

An increase in temperature has a dramatic effect on the distribution of energies, as can be seen in the graph below.

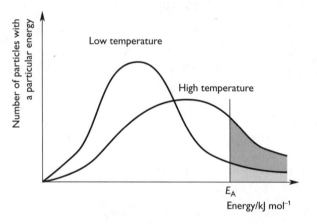

At the higher temperature, the distribution flattens and shifts to the right because:
- there are fewer particles with low energy
- a greater proportion of particles have energy that exceeds the activation energy

Increasing temperature increases the number of particles with energy greater than or equal to the activation energy ($E \geqslant E_a$) which means that at high temperature there are more particles with sufficient energy to react. Therefore, the reaction is faster.

Catalyst

Catalysts work by lowering the activation energy for the reaction. This is illustrated below.

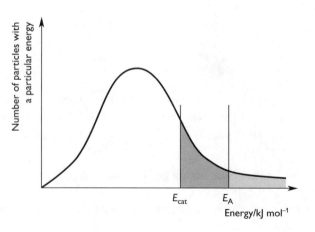

E_a is the activation energy of the uncatalysed reaction. E_{cat} is the activation energy of the catalysed reaction.

Reaction rate

The rate of a reaction is usually measured as the change in concentration of a reaction species with time. The units of rate are $mol\,dm^{-3}\,s^{-1}$.

Measuring rates from graphs

Consider the reaction:

$$A + B \longrightarrow C + D$$

It is possible to measure the rate of disappearance of either A or B or the rate of appearance of either of the products, C or D.

The rate of *decrease* in concentration of $A = -\dfrac{d[A]}{dt}$

The rate of *increase* in concentration of $C = \dfrac{d[C]}{dt}$

The gradient of the concentration–time graph is a measure of the rate of a reaction.

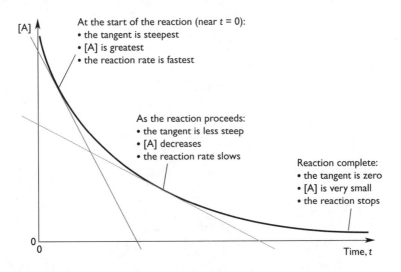

At the start of the reaction (near $t = 0$):
- the tangent is steepest
- [A] is greatest
- the reaction rate is fastest

As the reaction proceeds:
- the tangent is less steep
- [A] decreases
- the reaction rate slows

Reaction complete:
- the tangent is zero
- [A] is very small
- the reaction stops

Rate equation and orders of reaction

The rate equation of a reaction shows how the rate is affected by the concentration of each reactant and can only be determined by experiment.

In general, for a reaction $A + B \longrightarrow C + D$, the reaction rate is given by:

$$rate = k[A]^m[B]^n$$

- k is the **rate constant** of the reaction
- m and n are the **orders of reaction** with respect to A and B

The *overall* order of reaction is $m + n$.

The rate constant k indicates the rate of the reaction:
- a large value of k means a fast rate of reaction
- a small value of k means a slow rate of reaction

An increase in temperature speeds up the rate of most reactions by increasing the rate constant k.

Determination of orders from graphs

Concentration–time graphs

A concentration–time graph is plotted by measuring the concentration of a reactant or product at various times during the course of an experiment. The shape of this graph indicates the order of the reaction, which is determined by measuring the **half-life** of a reactant. The half-life of a reactant is the time taken for its concentration to halve during a reaction.

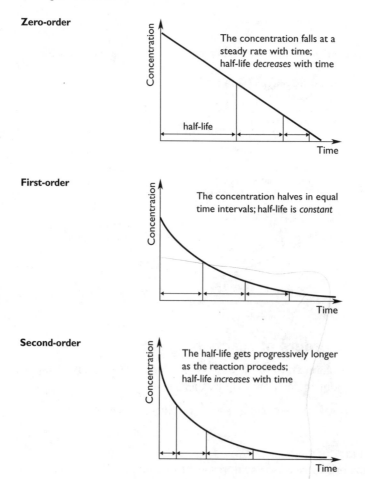

Zero-order

The concentration falls at a steady rate with time; half-life *decreases* with time

half-life

First-order

The concentration halves in equal time intervals; half-life is *constant*

Second-order

The half-life gets progressively longer as the reaction proceeds; half-life *increases* with time

Rate–concentration graphs

A concentration–time graph is first plotted and tangents are drawn at several time values on it, giving values of reaction rates. A second graph is then plotted of rate against concentration. The shape of this graph indicates the order of the reaction.

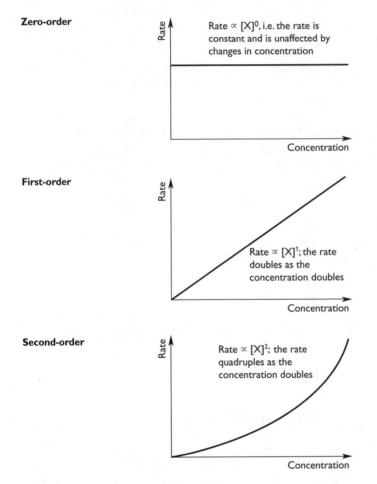

Zero-order

Rate $\propto [X]^0$, i.e. the rate is constant and is unaffected by changes in concentration

First-order

Rate $\propto [X]^1$; the rate doubles as the concentration doubles

Second-order

Rate $\propto [X]^2$; the rate quadruples as the concentration doubles

The second-order relationship can be confirmed by plotting a graph of rate against $[X]^2$, which gives a straight line.

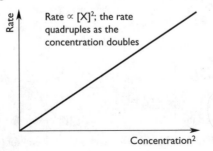

Rate $\propto [X]^2$; the rate quadruples as the concentration doubles

Measuring rates using the initial rates method

For a reaction A + B $\longrightarrow$ C + D, experiments are carried out using different *initial* concentrations of the reactants A and B.

When changing only one variable at a time, two series of experiments are required:
- The concentration of A is changed while the concentration of B is kept constant.
- The concentration of B is changed while the concentration of A is kept constant.

For each experiment, a concentration–time graph is plotted. The initial rate of the reaction is the gradient of the tangent drawn at time zero. A typical set of results is given in the table below.

Experiment	[A(aq)]/mol dm^{-3}	[B(aq)]/mol dm^{-3}	Initial rate/mol dm^{-3} s^{-1}
1	1.0×10^{-2}	1.0×10^{-2}	4.0×10^{-3}
2	2.0×10^{-2}	1.0×10^{-2}	1.6×10^{-2}
3	2.0×10^{-2}	2.0×10^{-2}	3.2×10^{-2}

The order of reaction with respect to A:
- Comparing experiments 1 and 2 — [B(aq)] is constant and [A(aq)] is varied.
- [A(aq)] has doubled and the rate has quadrupled. Therefore, the reaction is second-order with respect to A(aq).

The order of reaction with respect to B:
- Comparing experiments 2 and 3 — [A(aq)] is constant and [B(aq)] is varied.
- [B(aq)] has doubled and the rate has doubled. Therefore, the reaction is first-order with respect to B(aq).

The rate equation for the reaction is:
rate = $k[A]^2[B]$

The overall order of the reaction is (2 + 1) = third-order.

The rate constant
Rearranging the rate equation: $k = \dfrac{\text{rate}}{[A]^2[B]}$

Substitute values from one of the experiments. Here, experiment 1 has been used.

$$k = \frac{(4.0 \times 10^{-3})}{(1.0 \times 10^{-2})^2 (1.0 \times 10^{-2})} = 4.0 \times 10^3 \, \text{dm}^6 \text{mol}^{-2} \, \text{s}^{-1}$$

The *units* of a rate constant depend upon the rate equation for the reaction.

Order	Rate equation	Units of k
First	Rate = $k[A]$	s^{-1}
Second	Rate = $k[A]^2$ or $k[A][B]$	dm^3 mol^{-1} s^{-1}
Third	Rate = $k[A]^3$ or $k[A]^2[B]$	dm^6 mol^{-2} s^{-1}

Determination of reaction mechanisms

The **rate-determining** step is defined as the slowest step in the reaction.

The rate equation can provide clues about a likely reaction mechanism by identifying the slowest stage of a reaction sequence. For instance, if the rate equation is:

rate = $k[A]^2[B]$

the slow step will involve *two* molecules of A and *one* molecule of B. If the rate equation is:

rate = $k[A][B]^2$

the slow step will involve *one* molecule of A and *two* molecules of B.

The orders in the rate equation match the number of species involved in the rate-determining step.

Reaction mechanisms often involve many separate steps. You may be asked to use the rate equation and the balanced equation to predict a mechanism that contains two steps. In a two-step mechanism, the rate equation indicates the number of molecules of each reactant involved in the slow step. The slow step plus the fast step gives the balanced equation.

Example

$$2H_2(g) + 2NO(g) \longrightarrow 2H_2O(l) + N_2(g)$$

The rate equation is:

rate = $k[H_2(g)][NO(g)]^2$

Predict a two-step mechanism.

Answer

Remember: slow step + fast step = balanced equation

The rate equation tells us that the slow step involves 1 mol $H_2(g)$ and 2 mols $NO(g)$. The balanced equation is given in the question, so just copy it down. A possible two-step mechanism is:

Slow step: $1H_2(g) + 2NO(g) \longrightarrow H_2O(l) + N_2(g) + \bullet O(g)$

Fast step: $1H_2(g) + \bullet O(g) \longrightarrow H_2O(l)$

Balanced equation: $2H_2(g) + 2NO(g) \longrightarrow 2H_2O(l) + N_2(g)$

How far?

Overview of required AS chemistry

You should revise the chemical equilibrium section of Module 2813, which is covered in the guide to Unit 3. This introduces the idea of a reversible reaction, a dynamic equilibrium and Le Chatelier's principle.

In a **reversible reaction**, the reagents react to form products and the products react to re-form the reagents. The reaction proceeds in both forward and reverse directions, which leads to the formation of a dynamic equilibrium.

A **dynamic equilibrium** is reached when the rate of the forward reaction equals the rate of the reverse reaction. The composition of the mixture remains constant but the reagents and products are constantly interchanging.

Le Chatelier's principle

Le Chatelier's principle states that if a closed system under equilibrium is subjected to a change in temperature, pressure or concentration, the system will move to *minimise* the effect of the change.

Effect of a change in temperature

The effect of changing temperature depends on whether the forward reaction is exothermic or endothermic.

- If the forward reaction is exothermic, $-\Delta H$, increasing the temperature moves the equilibrium position to the left.
- If the forward reaction is endothermic, $+\Delta H$, increasing the temperature moves the equilibrium position to the right.

Effect of a change in pressure

The effect of changing pressure depends on the number of molecules of gas on each side of the equilibrium.

- Increasing pressure moves the position of the equilibrium to the side with fewer gas molecules.
- Decreasing pressure moves the position of the equilibrium to the side with most gas molecules.

Effect of a change in concentration

The effect of increasing concentration of either a reagent or a product is to move the position of the equilibrium in the opposite direction.

Effect of a catalyst

Catalysts speed up the rate of the reaction but do *not* change the equilibrium position.

> **Task**   You should be able to use Le Chatelier's principle to deduce what happens to an equilibrium when it is subjected to stated changes. Try the two examples that follow and check the answers, which are on page 59. If you have difficulty with these, check your AS notes or seek help from your teacher.
>
> (1) $2NO_2(g) \rightleftharpoons N_2O_4(g)$ $\Delta H = +100 \, kJ \, mol^{-1}$
> (i) Temperature is increased. go towards left
> (ii) Pressure is increased. go towards right
> (iii) A catalyst is used. hurry reaction to eqm
> (iv) Concentration of NO_2 is increased. go towards left
> (2) $I_2(g) + H_2(g) \rightleftharpoons 2HI(g)$ $\Delta H = -35.0 \, kJ \, mol^{-1}$
> (i) Temperature is increased. go right exothermic
> (ii) Pressure is increased. go nowhere

(iii) A catalyst is used.

(iv) Concentration of H_2 is increased.

The equilibrium constant, K_c

The exact position of equilibrium is calculated using the equilibrium law.

The equilibrium law

K_c is the equilibrium constant in terms of equilibrium concentrations. The equilibrium law states that, for a reaction:

$$aA + bB \rightleftharpoons cC + dD$$

$$K_c = \frac{[C]^c[D]^d}{[A]^a[B]^b}$$

- [A], [B], [C] and [D] are the **equilibrium concentrations** of the reactants and products of the reaction.
- Each product and reactant has its equilibrium concentration raised to the *power* of its **balancing number** (a, b, c and d) in the equation.
- The equilibrium concentrations of the *products* are multiplied together on *top* of the fraction.
- The equilibrium concentrations of the *reactants* are multiplied together on the *bottom* of the fraction.

Working out K_c

$$H_2(g) + I_2(g) \rightleftharpoons 2HI(g)$$

Applying the equilibrium law:

$$K_c = \frac{[HI(g)]^2}{[H_2(g)][I_2(g)]}$$

At equilibrium: $[H_2(g)] = 0.012\,mol\,dm^{-3}$; $[I_2(g)] = 0.001\,mol\,dm^{-3}$; $[HI(g)] = 0.025\,mol\,dm^{-3}$.

$$K_c = \frac{(0.025)^2}{0.012 \times 0.001} = 52.1$$

Units of K_c

The units of K_c depend upon the equilibrium expression for the reaction.

Each concentration value is replaced by its units:

$$K_c = \frac{[HI(g)]^2}{[H_2(g)][I_2(g)]}$$

$$= \frac{(mol\,dm^{-3})^2}{(mol\,dm^{-3})\,(mol\,dm^{-3})}$$

For this equilibrium, the units cancel and K_c has no units.

Properties of K_c

K_c indicates how *far* a reaction proceeds but tells us nothing about how *fast* the reaction occurs. The size of K_c indicates the extent of a chemical equilibrium.

- If K_c is big ($K_c = 1000$), the equilibrium lies far to the right and a high percentage of product is formed.
- If K_c is small ($K_c = 1 \times 10^{-3}$), the equilibrium lies far to the left and a low percentage of product is formed.
- If $K_c = 1$, the equilibrium lies halfway between reactants and products.

Changing K_c

K_c is a constant *but* it is temperature dependent — it can be changed by altering the temperature. K_c is unaffected by changes in concentration or pressure.

- In an exothermic reaction, K_c decreases with increasing temperature because raising the temperature reduces the equilibrium yield of products.
- In an endothermic reaction, K_c increases with increasing temperature because raising the temperature increases the equilibrium yield of products.

Experimental determination of K_c

The equilibrium constant, K_c, can be determined from experimental results. The example below shows how to answer a typical question.

The ethyl ethanoate esterification equilibrium

0.200 mol CH_3COOH and 0.100 mol C_2H_5OH were mixed together with a trace of acid catalyst in a total volume of 200 cm³. The mixture was allowed to reach equilibrium:

$$CH_3COOH + C_2H_5OH \rightleftharpoons CH_3COOC_2H_5 + H_2O$$

Analysis of the mixture showed that 0.115 mol of CH_3COOH were present at equilibrium. Calculate the equilibrium constant, K_c.

Step 1: *Find the change in moles of each component in the equilibrium.*

From the information given:
The number of moles of CH_3COOH that reacted = 0.200 − 0.115 = 0.085.

The balanced equation tells us the molar ratio of the reactants and the products.

Balanced equation:	CH_3COOH +	C_2H_5OH $\rightleftharpoons$	$CH_3COOC_2H_5$ +	H_2O
Molar ratio:	1 mol	1 mol	1 mol	1 mol
Change in moles:	−0.085	−0.085	+0.085	+0.085

Step 2: *Determine the equilibrium concentrations of each component.*

	CH_3COOH +	C_2H_5OH $\rightleftharpoons$	$CH_3COOC_2H_5$ +	H_2O
Initial amount/mol	0.200	0.100	0	0
Change in moles	−0.085	−0.085	+0.085	+0.085
Equilibrum amount/mol	0.115	0.015	0.085	0.085
Equilibrium concentration/ mol dm⁻³	$\dfrac{0.115}{0.20}$	$\dfrac{0.015}{0.20}$	$\dfrac{0.085}{0.20}$	$\dfrac{0.085}{0.20}$

Step 3: *Write the expression for K_c, substitute values and calculate K_c.*

$$K_c = \frac{[CH_3COOC_2H_5][H_2O]}{[CH_3COOH][C_2H_5OH]}$$

$$= \frac{0.085/0.20 \times 0.085/0.20}{0.115/0.20 \times 0.015/0.20}$$

$$= \frac{0.425 \times 0.425}{0.575 \times 0.075}$$

$$= 4.19$$

K_c has no units because the equilibrium concentration units cancel.

The equilibrium constant, K_p

Equilibria involving gases are usually expressed in terms of K_p, the equilibrium constant in terms of partial pressures.

Partial pressure: in a gas mixture, the partial pressure of a gas, p, is the contribution that a gas makes towards the total pressure, P_T.

Mole fraction: the mole fraction of gas A, in a gas mixture, x_A, is:

$$x_A = \frac{\text{number of moles of A}}{\text{total number of moles in gas mixture}}$$

The partial pressure of A, p_A, is the mole fraction of A × total pressure:

$$p_A = x_A \times P_T$$

As with all fractions, the sum of the mole fractions in a mixture must equal one.

The equilibrium constant, K_p, is written in a similar way to K_c but with partial pressures replacing concentration.

Consider the equilibrium:

$$H_2(g) + I_2(g) \rightleftharpoons 2HI(g)$$

$$K_p = \frac{pHI^2}{pH_2 \times pI_2}$$

- p is the equilibrium partial pressure.
- Suitable units for partial pressures are kilopascals (kPa) or pascals (Pa). The same unit must be used for all the gases in the reaction.
- The power to which the partial pressure is raised is the balancing number in the chemical equation.

Species other than gases are not included in the expression for K_p. So, for the equilibrium:

$$Fe_3O_4(s) + 4H_2(g) \rightleftharpoons 3Fe(s) + 4H_2O(g)$$

$$K_p = \frac{[H_2O(g)]^4}{[H_2(g)]^4}$$

Working out K_p

An equilibrium mixture contains 13.5 mol $N_2(g)$, 3.6 mol $H_2(g)$, and 1.0 mol $NH_3(g)$. The total equilibrium pressure is 200 kPa. Calculate K_p.

Step 1: *Find the mole fractions.*

Total number of gas moles = 13.5 + 3.6 + 1.0 = 18.1

$$pN_2 = \frac{13.5}{18.1} = 0.746$$

$$pH_2 = \frac{3.6}{18.1} = 0.199$$

$$pNH_3 = \frac{1.0}{18.1} = 0.055$$

The mole fractions of the gases should always add up to one. In this case:
    0.746 + 0.199 + 0.055 = 1

Step 2: *Find the partial pressures.*

$$pN_2 = \frac{13.5}{18.1} \times 200 = 149\,kPa$$

$$pH_2 = \frac{3.6}{18.1} \times 200 = 40\,kPa$$

$$pNH_3 = \frac{1.0}{18.1} \times 200 = 11\,kPa$$

The partial pressures of the gases should always add up to the total pressure. In this case:
    149 + 40 + 11 = 200 kPa

Step 3: *Calculate K_p.*

$$N_2(g) + 3H_2(g) \rightleftharpoons 2NH_3(g)$$

$$K_p = \frac{pNH_3{}^2}{pN_2 \times pH_2{}^3}$$

$$K_p = \frac{11^2}{149 \times 40^3} = 1.27 \times 10^{-5}$$

Step 4: *Determine the units of K_p.*

The units for K_p are found by replacing each partial pressure value in the K_p expression by its units.

Substituting units: $K_p = \dfrac{kPa^2}{kPa\ kPa^3}$

Therefore, the units of K_p are kPa^{-2}.

$$K_p = 1.27 \times 10^{-5}\,kPa^{-2}$$

Task It is essential that you are able to write expressions for both K_c and K_p. You should be able to deduce the units, if any, for each expression. Complete the examples below and check your answers on page 59.

(1) $2NO_2(g) \rightleftharpoons N_2O_4(g)$

(2) $CH_4(g) + H_2O(g) \rightleftharpoons CO(g) + 3H_2(g)$

(3) $N_2(g) + 3H_2(g) \rightleftharpoons 2NH_3(g)$

(4) $Br_2(g) + H_2(g) \rightleftharpoons 2HBr(g)$

Acids, bases and buffers

Acids were introduced in AS Module 2813: How Far, How Fast? You should be able to define an acid as a proton donor and write balanced formulae and ionic equations for the reactions of acids. These are outlined in Unit 3 of this series.

Brønsted–Lowry acids and bases

An acid–base reaction involves proton transfer. A Brønsted–Lowry acid is a proton donor and a Brønsted–Lowry base is a proton acceptor.

Acid–base pairs

A molecule of an acid contains a hydrogen that can be released as a positive hydrogen ion or proton, H^+.

Acids and bases can be linked as **conjugate acid–base pairs**. Some common conjugate acid–base pairs are shown in the table below:

Conjugate pairs	
Acid	**Base**
CH_3COOH	CH_3COO^-
NH_4^+	NH_3
H_3O^+	H_2O

Each conjugate acid–base pair differs by H^+. By mixing an acid with a base, an equilibrium is set up between *two* acid–base conjugate pairs.

In the forward reaction $\longrightarrow$

$CH_3COOH(aq)$ donates an H^+ to the water and, therefore, behaves as an acid.
H_2O accepts an H^+ from $CH_3COOH(aq)$ and, therefore, behaves as a base.

$$CH_3COOH(aq) + H_2O(l) \rightleftharpoons H_3O^+(aq) + CH_3COO^-(aq)$$

$\longleftarrow$ *In the reverse reaction*

$H_3O^+(aq)$ donates an H^+ to the $CH_3COO^-(aq)$ and, therefore, behaves as an acid.
$CH_3COO^-(aq)$ accepts an H^+ from $H_3O^+(aq)$ and, therefore, behaves as a base.

$CH_3COOH(aq)$ and $CH_3COO^-(aq)$ form an acid–base conjugate pair, and $H_3O^+(aq)$ and $H_2O(l)$ form a second acid–base conjugate pair.

Strength of acids and bases

The acid–base equilibrium of an acid, HA, in water is:

$$HA(aq) + H_2O(l) \rightleftharpoons H_3O^+(aq) + A^-(aq)$$

To emphasise the loss of a proton, H^+, by **dissociation**, the equilibrium can be expressed as:

$$HA(aq) \rightleftharpoons H^+(aq) + A^-(aq)$$

The *strength* of an acid shows the *extent of dissociation* into H^+ and A^-.

Strong acids

Strong acids, such as nitric acid (HNO_3), are good proton donors.

$$HNO_3(aq) \rightleftharpoons H^+(aq) + NO_3^-(aq)$$

The equilibrium position is well to the right. There is almost complete dissociation and it is usual to write the equation as:

$$HNO_3(aq) \longrightarrow H^+(aq) + NO_3^-(aq)$$

Weak acids

Weak acids, such as ethanoic acid (CH_3COOH), are poor proton donors. The equilibrium position is well to the left.

$$CH_3COOH(aq) \rightleftharpoons H^+(aq) + CH_3COO^-(aq)$$

There is only partial dissociation.

The acid dissociation constant, K_a

The extent of acid dissociation is shown by an equilibrium constant called the **acid dissociation constant**, K_a.

$$HA(aq) \rightleftharpoons H^+(aq) + A^-(aq)$$

$$K_a = \frac{[H^+(aq)][A^-(aq)]}{[HA(aq)]}$$

Units: $K_a = \dfrac{(mol\,dm^{-3})^2}{(mol\,dm^{-3})} = mol\,dm^{-3}$

- A high K_a value shows that the extent of dissociation is large — the acid is strong.
- A low K_a value shows that the extent of dissociation is small — the acid is weak.

The pH scale

The concentration of $H^+(aq)$ ions in acid solutions varies widely between about $10\,mol\,dm^{-3}$ and about $1 \times 10^{-15}\,mol\,dm^{-3}$. The pH scale is used to overcome the problem of this wide range of numbers. It is a logarithmic scale — each change of one unit on the pH scale corresponds to a tenfold change in the $H^+(aq)$ concentration.

content guidance

pH	0	1	2	3	4	5	6	7	8	9	10	11	12	13	14
[H⁺]	1	10^{-1}	10^{-2}	10^{-3}	10^{-4}	10^{-5}	10^{-6}	10^{-7}	10^{-8}	10^{-9}	10^{-10}	10^{-11}	10^{-12}	10^{-13}	10^{-14}

more acidic ←   neutral   → more alkaline

pH is defined by the equation:

$$pH = -\log_{10}[H^+(aq)]$$

You should be able to convert pH to $H^+(aq)$ and vice versa using the relationships below:

$$pH = -\log_{10}[H^+(aq)] \text{ and } [H^+(aq)] = 10^{-pH}$$

Calculating the pH of strong acids

For a strong acid, we can assume complete dissociation and the concentration of $H^+(aq)$ can be found from the acid concentration.

Example 1

A strong acid, HA, has a concentration of $0.020\,mol\,dm^{-3}$. What is the pH?

The acid completely dissociates. Therefore:

$$[H^+(aq)] = 0.020\,mol\,dm^{-3}$$
$$pH = -\log_{10}[H^+(aq)] = -\log_{10}(0.020) = 1.7$$

Example 2

A strong acid, HA, has a pH of 2.4. What is the concentration of $H^+(aq)$?

The acid completely dissociates. Therefore:

$$[H^+(aq)] = 10^{-pH} = 10^{-2.4}\,mol\,dm^{-3}$$
$$[H^+(aq)] = 3.98 \times 10^{-3}\,mol\,dm^{-3}$$

Calculating the pH of weak acids

Weak acids do not dissociate completely. To calculate the pH of a weak acid, you need to know:

- the concentration of the acid
- the acid dissociation constant, K_a

Assumptions and approximations

In the equilibrium of a weak aqueous acid, HA(aq):

$$HA(aq) \rightleftharpoons H^+(aq) + A^-(aq)$$

Assume that only a very small proportion of HA dissociates. Therefore:

$$[HA(aq)]_{equilibrium} \approx [HA(aq)]_{start}$$

Assume that there is a negligible proportion of $H^+(aq)$ from the ionisation of water. Therefore:

$$[H^+(aq)] \approx [A^-(aq)]$$

Using these approximations:

$$K_a = \frac{[H^+(aq)][A^-(aq)]}{[HA(aq)]} \approx \frac{[H^+(aq)]^2}{[HA(aq)]}$$

Example

For a weak acid, [HA (aq)] = 0.200 mol dm^{-3}; K$_a$ = 1.70 × 10^{-4} mol dm^{-3} at 25 °C. Calculate the pH.

$$K_a = \frac{[H^+(aq)][A^-(aq)]}{[HA(aq)]} \approx \frac{[H^+(aq)]^2}{[HA(aq)]}$$

Therefore:

$$1.70 \times 10^{-4} = \frac{[H^+(aq)]^2}{0.200}$$

$$1.70 \times 10^{-4} \times 0.200 = [H^+(aq)]^2$$
$$[H^+(aq)] = \sqrt{(1.70 \times 10^{-4} \times 0.200} = 5.83 \times 10^{-3} = 0.00583$$
$$pH = -\log_{10}[H^+(aq)]$$
$$= -\log_{10}(0.00583) = 2.23$$

An alternative way of doing this type of calculation is to use the equation:
$$pH = -\log_{10}\sqrt{(K_a \text{ of HA} \times \text{concentration of HA})}$$
or
$$pH = -\log_{10}\sqrt{(K_a \times [HA])}$$

The same calculation can now be carried out in a single step:
$$pH = -\log_{10}\sqrt{1.70 \times 10^{-4} \times 0.200}$$
$$pH = 2.23$$

K_a and pK_a

As with [H$^+$(aq)] and pH, K_a is often expressed as the logarithmic form, pK_a, which is defined as:
$$pK_a = -\log_{10}K_a$$

On this logarithmic scale, each change of 1 unit on the pK_a scale corresponds to a ten-fold change in K_a. Like pH, pK_a can be used as a guide to acidity. The lower the pK_a value, the stronger the acid.

Acid	Formula	K_a/mol dm^{-3}	pK_a
Ethanoic acid	CH_3COOH	1.7×10^{-5}	$-\log_{10}(1.7 \times 10^{-5}) = 4.8$
Benzoic acid	C_6H_5COOH	6.3×10^{-5}	$-\log_{10}(6.3 \times 10^{-5}) = 4.2$

This indicates that benzoic acid is a stronger acid than ethanoic acid.

The ionic product of water, K_w

Water ionises very slightly, acting as both an acid and a base:

$H_2O(l)$	+	$H_2O(l)$	$\rightleftharpoons$	$H_3O^+(aq)$	+	$OH^-(aq)$
Acid 1		Base 2		Acid 2		Base 1
(donates proton)		(accepts proton)		(donates proton)		(accepts proton)

Or, more simply,

$$H_2O(l) \rightleftharpoons H^+(aq) + OH^-(aq)$$

In water, a very small proportion of molecules dissociate into $H^+(aq)$ and $OH^-(aq)$ ions.

Treating water as a weak acid:

$$K_a = \frac{[H^+(aq)][OH^-(aq)]}{[H_2O(l)]}$$

Rearranging gives:

$$K_a \times [H_2O(l)] = [H^+(aq)][OH^-(aq)]$$

- $K_a \times [H_2O(l)]$ is a constant, K_w, and is called the **ionic product** of water
- $K_w = [H^+(aq)][OH^-(aq)] = 1.0 \times 10^{-14}$ mol^2 dm^{-6} (at 25°C)
- K_w is temperature-dependent and is equal to 1.0×10^{-14} mol^2 dm^{-6} at 25°C (298 K) only.
  - At 10°C (283 K), $K_w = 2.9 \times 10^{-15}$ mol^2 dm^{-6}
  - At 40°C (313 K), $K_w = 2.9 \times 10^{-14}$ mol^2 dm^{-6}

Use of K_w to calculate the pH of water
Example 1
At 25°C:

$$K_w = [H^+(aq)][OH^-(aq)] = 1.0 \times 10^{-14} \text{ mol}^2 \text{dm}^{-6}$$

Assuming that $[H^+(aq)] = [OH^-(aq)]$, then $K_w = [H^+(aq)]^2 = 1.0 \times 10^{-14}$ mol^2 dm^{-6}

$[H^+(aq)] = 1.0 \times 10^{-7}$ mol dm^{-3}

$pH = -\log_{10}[H^+(aq)] = -\log_{10}(1.0 \times 10^{-7})$

$pH = 7.0$

However, since K_w changes with temperature, it follows that the pH of water is equal to 7 at 25°C only.

Example 2
At 10°C:

$$K_w = [H^+(aq)][OH^-(aq)] = 2.9 \times 10^{-15} \text{ mol}^2 \text{dm}^{-6}$$

Assuming that $[H^+(aq)] = [OH^-(aq)]$, then $K_w = [H^+(aq)]^2 = 2.9 \times 10^{-15}$ mol^2 dm^{-6}

$[H^+(aq)] = 5.4 \times 10^{-8}$ mol dm^{-3}

$pH = -\log_{10}[H^+(aq)] = -\log_{10}(5.4 \times 10^{-8})$

$pH = 7.3$

Example 3
At 40°C:

$$K_w = [H^+(aq)][OH^-(aq)] = 2.9 \times 10^{-14} \text{ mol}^2 \text{dm}^{-6}$$

Assuming that $[H^+(aq)] = [OH^-(aq)]$, then $K_w = [H^+(aq)]^2 = 2.9 \times 10^{-14}$ mol^2 dm^{-6}

$[H^+(aq)] = 1.7 \times 10^{-7}$ mol dm^{-3}

$pH = -\log_{10}[H^+(aq)] = -\log_{10}(1.7 \times 10^{-7})$

$pH = 6.8$

Use of K_w to calculate the pH of strong alkalis

The pH of a strong alkali, BOH, can be calculated from the concentration of the alkali and the ionic product of water, K_w.

Example

A strong alkali, BOH, has a concentration of $0.50 \, mol \, dm^{-3}$. What is the pH at $25 °C$?

BOH dissociates completely. Therefore:

$[OH^-(aq)] = [BOH] = 0.50 \, mol \, dm^{-3}$

First find $[H^+]$ using K_w and $[OH^-]$:

$$K_w = [H^+(aq)][OH^-(aq)] = 1 \times 10^{-14} \, mol^2 \, dm^{-6}$$

$$[H^+(aq)] = \frac{K_w}{[OH^-(aq)]}$$

$$= \frac{1 \times 10^{-14}}{0.50}$$

$$= 2 \times 10^{-14} \, mol \, dm^{-3}$$

$$pH = -\log_{10}[H^+(aq)]$$

$$= -\log_{10}(2 \times 10^{-14}) = 13.7$$

pH changes and indicators

An indicator changes colour at the end point of a titration, because of the change in pH. Many indicators are weak acids and can be represented as HIn. The weak acid, HIn, and its conjugate base, In⁻, have different colours. For example, for methyl orange:

$$\begin{array}{ccccc} (Red) & & & (Yellow) \\ HIn(aq) & \rightleftharpoons & H^+(aq) & + & In^-(aq) \\ (Weak \, acid) & & & & (Conjugate \\ & & & & base) \end{array}$$

At the end point of a titration, HIn and In⁻ are present in equal concentrations.

Using methyl orange as indicator:
- at the end point $[HIn] = [In^-]$
- the colour at the end point is orange, from equal proportions of red HIn and yellow In⁻
- the pH at the end point is called the pK_{ind} of the indicator

pH ranges for common indicators

An indicator changes colour over a range of about two pH units within which is the pK_{ind} value of the indicator.

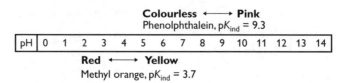

Colourless ←——→ Pink
Phenolphthalein, $pK_{ind} = 9.3$

| pH | 0 | 1 | 2 | 3 | 4 | 5 | 6 | 7 | 8 | 9 | 10 | 11 | 12 | 13 | 14 |

Red ←——→ Yellow
Methyl orange, $pK_{ind} = 3.7$

Choosing an indicator

When the acid and the base have completely reacted, this is known as the **equivalence point**. At the equivalence point of the titration, there is a sharp change in pH for a very small addition of acid or base.

The choice of a suitable indicator is best shown using **titration curves**, which show the changes in pH during a titration.

Key features of titration curves

- The pH changes rapidly at the near vertical portion of the titration curve. This is the end point of the titration.
- The sharp change in pH is brought about by a very small addition of alkali, typically the addition of one drop.
- The indicator is only suitable if its pK_{ind} value is within the pH range of the near vertical portion of the titration curve.

Choosing an indicator using titration curves

On the titration curves below:

- different combinations of strong and weak acids have been used
- the pK_{ind} values are shown for the indicators methyl orange and phenolphthalein

Strong acid/strong alkali

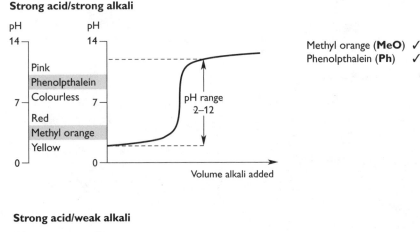

Methyl orange (**MeO**) ✓
Phenolphthalein (**Ph**) ✓

Strong acid/weak alkali

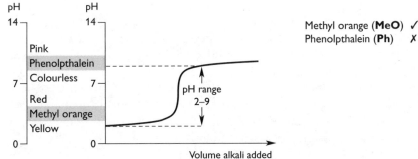

Methyl orange (**MeO**) ✓
Phenolphthalein (**Ph**) ✗

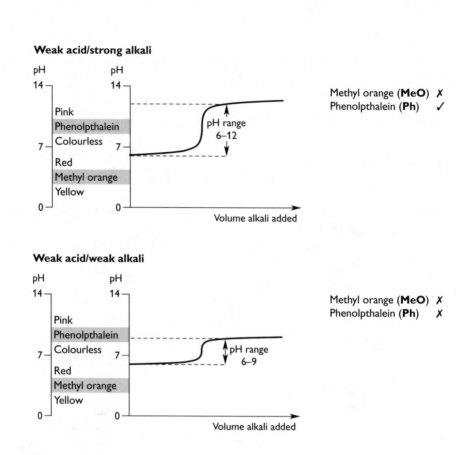

Weak acid/strong alkali

Methyl orange (**MeO**) ✗
Phenolpthalein (**Ph**) ✓

Weak acid/weak alkali

Methyl orange (**MeO**) ✗
Phenolpthalein (**Ph**) ✗

Buffer solutions

A buffer solution resists changes in pH during the addition of an acid or an alkali. The buffer solution maintains a near constant pH by removing most of any acid or alkali that is added to the solution.

Making a buffer solution

A buffer solution is a mixture of a weak acid, HA, and its conjugate base, A^-:

$$HA(aq) \rightleftharpoons H^+(aq) + A^-(aq)$$
(Weak acid)   (Conjugate base)

An example of a common buffer solution is a mixture of CH_3COOH (the weak acid) and $CH_3COO^-Na^+$ (the conjugate base). A mixture of any weak acid and the salt of that weak acid can be used as a buffer. The pH at which the buffer operates depends on the K_a of the weak acid and the relative concentrations of the weak acid and the conjugate base. In a mixture of CH_3COOH and $CH_3COO^-Na^+$, the $CH_3COOH(aq)$ only partially dissociates, giving low concentrations of $CH_3COO^-(aq)$ and $H^+(aq)$, while the $CH_3COO^-Na^+$ totally dissociates, giving high concentrations of $CH_3COO^-(aq)$:

$$CH_3COOH(aq) \rightleftharpoons CH_3COO^-(aq) + H^+(aq)$$
$$CH_3COO^-Na^+(aq) \longrightarrow CH_3COO^-(aq) + Na^+(aq)$$

The high CH_3COO^-(aq) concentration forces the equilibrium to the left and results in the buffer solution containing a low concentration of H^+(aq) compared with high concentrations of CH_3COOH(aq) and CH_3COO^-(aq). These high concentrations of CH_3COOH(aq) and CH_3COO^-(aq) restrict any changes in pH.

How does a buffer act?

A buffer solution contains three important components:

- a high concentration of the weak acid, for example CH_3COOH(aq)
- a high concentration of the conjugate base, for example CH_3COO^-(aq)
- a low concentration of H^+(aq)

On addition of an acid, the concentration of H^+(aq) increases. The pH change is opposed because the high concentration of the conjugate base CH_3COO^-(aq) removes most of the added H^+(aq), by forming CH_3COOH(aq):

$$CH_3COO^-(aq) + H^+(aq) \longrightarrow CH_3COOH(aq)$$

On addition of an alkali, the concentration of OH^-(aq) increases. The added OH^-(aq) reacts with the high concentration of CH_3COOH(aq):

$$CH_3COOH(aq) + OH^-(aq) \longrightarrow H_2O(l) + CH_3COO^-(aq)$$

A buffer cannot cancel out the effect of all the acid or alkali that is added. The buffer removes most of any acid or alkali that is added and *minimises* any changes in pH.

Calculations involving buffer solutions

The pH of a buffer solution depends upon the acid dissociation constant, K_a, of the buffer system and the molar ratio of the weak acid and its conjugate base.

For a buffer containing the weak acid, HA, and its conjugate base, A^-:

$$K_a = \frac{[H^+(aq)]\ [A^-(aq)]}{[HA(aq)]}$$

$$\therefore\ [H^+(aq)] = K_a \times \frac{[HA(aq)]}{[A^-(aq)]} \quad \text{— Ratio of the weak acid and its conjugate base}$$

It follows that the pH of a buffer can be altered by adjusting the weak acid/conjugate base ratio.

Example

Calculate the pH of a buffer with concentrations of $0.10\ mol\ dm^{-3}$ CH_3COOH(aq) and $0.10\ mol\ dm^{-3}$ CH_3COO^-(aq). For CH_3COOH, $K_a = 1.7 \times 10^{-5}\ mol\ dm^{-3}$.

First, calculate $[H^+(aq)]$ using:

$$[H^+(aq)] = \frac{K_a \times [HA(aq)]}{[A^-(aq)]}$$

$$[H^+(aq)] = \frac{1.7 \times 10^{-5} \times 0.10}{0.10}$$

$$[H^+(aq)] = 1.7 \times 10^{-5}\ mol\ dm^{-3}$$

Then calculate the pH from $[H^+(aq)]$:

$$pH = -\log_{10}[H^+(aq)]$$
$$= -\log_{10}(1.7 \times 10^{-5})$$

pH of the buffer solution = 4.77

What happens to the pH if the concentration of $CH_3COOH(aq)$ is changed to 0.30 mol dm^{-3}?

First, calculate $[H^+(aq)]$ using:

$$[H^+(aq)] = \frac{K_a \times [HA(aq)]}{[A^-(aq)]}$$

$$[H^+(aq)] = \frac{1.7 \times 10^{-5} \times 0.30}{0.10}$$

$$[H^+(aq)] = 5.1 \times 10^{-5} \, mol \, dm^{-3}$$

Then calculate the pH from $[H^+(aq)]$:

$$pH = -\log_{10}[H^+(aq)]$$
$$= -\log_{10}(5.1 \times 10^{-5})$$

pH of the buffer solution = 4.29

Control of pH in the blood

In the human body, the blood plasma has a normal pH of 7.4. If the pH falls below 7.0 or rises above 7.8, the results could be fatal. The buffer systems in the blood are extremely effective and protect the fluid from large changes in pH. Blood contains a number of buffering systems, the major one being the carbonic acid–hydogen-carbonate (bicarbonate) system.

$$H_2O(l) + CO_2(g) \rightleftharpoons H_2CO_3 \rightleftharpoons HCO_3^- + H^+$$

H_2CO_3 is carbonic acid; HCO_3^- is hydrogen carbonate.

Adding an acid to the system increases the concentration of $H^+(aq)$, driving the equilibrium to the left. This increases the concentration of carbonic acid, which in turn is decreased by an increased breathing rate. More CO_2 is exhaled, resulting in the H_2CO_3 moving further to the left to replace the CO_2. The two equilibria together resist the increase in acidity.

Adding an alkali to the system decreases the concentration of $H^+(aq)$, driving the equilibrium to the right. This decreases the concentration of carbonic acid, which in turn is increased by a decreased rate of breathing. Less CO_2 is exhaled, resulting in the H_2CO_3 being replaced. The two equilibria together resist the increase in alkalinity.

Common uses of buffers

Soaps and detergents are alkaline and irritate the skin and eyes. Shampoo often contains a mixture of citric acid (a weak acid) and sodium citrate (the conjugate base), which acts as a buffer. The ratio of the acid and the conjugate base is adjusted so that the pH is maintained at about pH 5.5, which is approximately the pH of skin.

Babies often suffer from nappy rash because dirty nappies contain ammonia, which is a weak base and has a pH in the region 7–9. Bacteria multiply rapidly in the pH region 7–9 but not at all at pH 6. Baby lotions are buffered to around 5.5 to 6, the approximate pH of skin, so that the lotion protects the baby by preventing bacteria from multiplying.

Answers to task on page 36

(1) $5Fe^{2+} \longrightarrow 5Fe^{3+} + 5e^-$

$MnO_4^- + 8H^+ + 5e^- \longrightarrow Mn^{2+} + 4H_2O$

$5Fe^{2+} + MnO_4^- + 8H^+ \longrightarrow 5Fe^{3+} + Mn^{2+} + 4H_2O$

(2) $6Fe^{2+} \longrightarrow 6Fe^{3+} + 6e^-$

$Cr_2O_7^{2-} + 14H^+ + 6e^- \longrightarrow 2Cr^{3+} + 7H_2O$

$6Fe^{2+} + Cr_2O_7^{2-} + 14H^+ \longrightarrow 6Fe^{3+} + 2Cr^{3+} + 7H_2O$

(3) $2Fe^{2+} \longrightarrow 2Fe^{3+} + 2e^-$

$H_2O_2 + 2H^+ + 2e^- \longrightarrow 2H_2O$

$2Fe^{2+} + H_2O_2 + 2H^+ \longrightarrow 2Fe^{3+} + 2H_2O$

Answers to task on page 44

(1) $2NO_2(g) \rightleftharpoons N_2O_4(g)$ $\Delta H = +100\,kJ\,mol^{-1}$

  (i) Temperature is increased — *equilibrium moves to the right.*

  (ii) Pressure is increased — *equilibrium moves to the right.*

  (iii) A catalyst is used — *no effect.*

  (iv) Concentration of NO_2 is increased — *equilibrium moves to the right.*

(2) $I_2(g) + H_2(g) \rightleftharpoons 2HI(g)$ $\Delta H = -35.0\,kJ\,mol^{-1}$

  (i) Temperature is increased — *equilibrium moves to the left.*

  (ii) Pressure is increased — *no effect.*

  (iii) A catalyst is used — *no effect.*

  (iv) Concentration of H_2 is increased — *equilibrium moves to the right.*

Answers to task on page 49

(1) $K_c = \dfrac{[N_2O_4(g)]}{[NO_2(g)]^2}$ (units: $mol^{-1}\,dm^3$)

$K_p = \dfrac{pN_2O_4}{pNO_2{}^2}$ (units: kPa^{-1})

(2) $K_c = \dfrac{[CO(g)][H_2(g)]^3}{[CH_4(g)][H_2O(g)]}$ (units: $mol^2\,dm^{-6}$)

$K_p = \dfrac{pCO \times pH_2{}^3}{pCH_4 \times pH_2O}$ (units: kPa^2)

(3) $K_c = \dfrac{[NH_3(g)]^2}{[N_2(g)][H_2(g)]^3}$ (units: $mol^{-2}\,dm^6$)

$K_p = \dfrac{pNH_3{}^2}{pN_2 \times pH_2{}^3}$ (units: kPa^{-2})

(4) $K_c = \dfrac{[HBr(g)]^2}{[H_2(g)][Br_2(g)]}$ (units: none)

$K_p = \dfrac{pHBr^2}{pH_2 \times pBr_2}$ (units: none)

Questions
&
Answers

This section contains questions similar in style to those you can expect to see in Unit Tests 2815 and 2816. Questions 1–5 are for Unit 2815 and questions 6–10 are for Unit 2816. While there is a synoptic element to each of questions 6–9, question 10 is entirely synoptic. It does not relate directly to the specification. You are given data and have to use the data to answer the question.

The limited number of questions means that it is impossible to cover all the topics and all the question styles, but they should give you a flavour of what to expect. The responses that are shown are real students' answers to the questions.

There are several ways of using this section. You could:

- hide the answers to each question and try the question yourself. It needn't be a memory test — use your notes to see if you can actually make all the points that you ought to make
- check your answers against the candidates' responses and make an estimate of the likely standard of your response to each question
- check your answers against the examiner's comments to see if you can appreciate where you might have lost marks
- take on the role of the examiner and mark each of the responses yourself and then check to see if you agree with the marks awarded by the examiner

The Unit 2815 Component 01 Test lasts 60 minutes and there are 45 marks available, of which 30 are synoptic. The Unit 2816 Test lasts 75 minutes and all 60 marks are synoptic. Therefore, you must expect the questions to relate to other areas of the specification. Time is very tight, so it is important that you practise answering questions under timed conditions as part of your revision.

Examiner's comments

All candidate responses are followed by examiner's comments. These are preceded by the icon ℮ and indicate where credit is due. In the weaker answers, they also point out areas for improvement, specific problems and common errors such as lack of clarity, weak or non-existent development, irrelevance, misinterpretation of the question and mistaken meanings of terms.

Question 1

Born–Haber cycle

(a) (i) Explain what is meant by the term lattice enthalpy.   (2 marks)

(ii) Write an equation to illustrate the lattice enthalpy of magnesium chloride.   (2 marks)

Use the Born–Haber cycle below to answer the questions that follow.

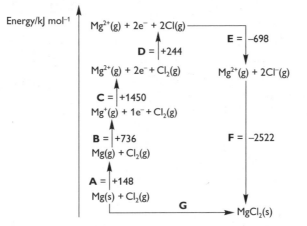

(b) (i) Identify which step represents the second ionisation energy of magnesium.   (1 mark)

(ii) Write an equation for the second ionisation energy of magnesium.   (1 mark)

(iii)Explain why the enthalpy value for the first ionisation energy of magnesium
     is about half the value of the second ionisation energy of magnesium.   (2 marks)

(c) (i) Write an equation for the first electron affinity of chlorine.   (1 mark)

(ii) State the energy, in $kJ\,mol^{-1}$, for the first electron affinity of chlorine. (1 mark)

(d) Calculate the enthalpy of formation of magnesium chloride.   (2 marks)

(e) The lattice enthalpy for magnesium bromide is $-2440\,kJ\,mol^{-1}$. Explain the
    difference in the lattice enthalpy between magnesium bromide and magnesium
    chloride.   (1 mark)

(f) Magnesium bromide and magnesium chloride are slightly soluble in water.
    Describe how you could distinguish between the two aqueous solutions. State
    the observations you would make.   (3 marks)

Total: 16 marks

■ ■ ■

Candidates' answers to Question 1

Candidate A

(a) (i) The lattice enthalpy is the enthalpy change when 1 mole of ionic solid is formed
         from its ions in the gas state.

Candidate B

(a) (i) It is the enthalpy released when the constituent gaseous ions form 1 mole of ionic solid.

e Both candidates score 2 marks. It is essential to learn straightforward definitions. The marks in this definition are for forming 1 mole of ionic solid ✓ from the gaseous ions ✓.

Candidate A

(a) (ii) $Mg^{2+}(g) + 2Cl^-(g) \longrightarrow MgCl_2(s)$

Candidate B

(a) (ii) $Mg^{2+} + 2Cl^-(g) \longrightarrow MgCl_2(s)$

e Candidate A gains both marks. Candidate B loses 1 mark by not putting the state symbol (g) after Mg^{2+}. Many candidates often forget to put the (g) after Mg — don't be caught out by this.

Candidate A

(b) (i) C

Candidate B

(b) (i) C

e Both candidates score the mark.

Candidate A

(b) (ii) $Mg^+(g) \longrightarrow Mg^{2+}(g) + 1e^-$

Candidate B

(b) (ii) $Mg \longrightarrow Mg^{2+} + 2e^-$

e Candidate A has made good use of the information in the question and gains the mark. Candidate B scores no marks for an incorrect equation. The state symbols are missing and, more importantly, it shows the first and second ionisation energies combined.

Candidate A

(b) (iii) Mg^+ is smaller than the Mg atom and therefore it is more difficult to remove the second electron.

Candidate B

(b) (iii) The second ionisation energy removes two electrons but the first ionisation energy removes only one electron; therefore it is twice as much.

e This is a difficult concept. The ease with which an electron can be removed depends on the attraction between the protons in the nucleus and the outer electrons. The three main factors that influence this are:
- distance from the nucleus
- shielding by inner shells
- proton-to-electron ratio

The shielding remains constant for the first and second ionisation energies of magnesium, but the distance from the nucleus and the proton:electron ratio both change. Candidate A scores 1 mark for explaining the variation in size/distance from the nucleus. Candidate B does not score — he/she has misinterpreted the question and jumped to the wrong conclusion.

Candidate A

(c) (i) $Cl(g) + 1e^- \longrightarrow Cl^-(g)$

Candidate B

(c) (i) $Cl(g) + e^- \longrightarrow Cl^-(g)$

🖉 Both candidates gain the mark.

Candidate A

(c) (ii) $-698\,kJ\,mol^{-1}$

Candidate B

(c) (ii) 349

🖉 Neither candidate gains the mark. Candidate A has used the information in the question but failed to spot that the enthalpy change given is for twice the first electron affinity of chlorine. Candidate B has spotted this and halved the numerical value. However, Candidate B scores no marks because the negative sign is missing.

Candidate A

(d) $\Delta H_f = 148 + 736 + 1450 + 244 - 698 - 2522 = -642\,kJ\,mol^{-1}$

Candidate B

(d) $-642\,kJ\,mol^{-1}$

🖉 Both candidates gain 2 marks. Candidate A shows better examination technique by showing the working.

Candidate A

(e) The lattice enthalpy depends on the ionic radius and the size of the charge. The charge for Cl^- and Br^- is the same but the Cl^- is smaller than the Br^- and therefore the attraction between the Mg^{2+} ion and the Cl^- will be bigger. Hence $MgCl_2$ will have a more negative lattice enthalpy than $MgBr_2$.

Candidate B

(e) The charge density of $Cl^- > Br^-$. The Mg^{2+} ion will be more attracted to the Cl^- ion and therefore the lattice enthalpy of $MgCl_2 > MgBr_2$.

🖉 Both candidates score the mark.

Candidate A

(f) Add silver nitrate to each and observe the colour of the precipitate. $MgCl_2$ would give a white solid and $MgBr_2$ would give a yellow solid.

Candidate B

(f) Both solutions would conduct electricity. If electricity is passed through the $MgCl_2$, a green gas will be evolved at the anode. With $MgBr_2$, an orange-brown liquid will be produced.

e This part of the question is synoptic — you have to recall information and knowledge from other areas of the specification. Candidate A has selected $AgNO_3$ as the reagent. This relates to Module 2811: Foundation Chemistry, where $AgNO_3$ is used to distinguish between the halides in the section on group 7. The observation for the chloride is correct but the colour for the bromide is incorrect. The iodide gives a yellow precipitate with $AgNO_3$ and the bromide gives a cream precipitate. Therefore, Candidate A scores 2 marks. Candidate B has given an unexpected answer, but nevertheless it is good chemistry and would probably work. Candidate B gains all 3 marks.

e **Both candidates demonstrate good understanding of this topic. Candidate A is more systematic and makes good use of the information in the question, scoring 13 out of 16 marks, which is grade-A standard. Candidate B scores 11, which is grade C. He/she has lost marks carelessly in parts (a)(ii) and (c)(ii) and shown poor understanding in parts (b)(ii) and (iii).**

question 2

Iron chemistry

(a) **What is meant by the term** *transition element?* (2 marks)

(b) **Complete the electronic configuration of the iron atom:**
$1s^2 2s^2 2p^6...$ (1 mark)

(c) **Give the electronic configurations of Fe^{2+} and Fe^{3+} ions.** (2 marks)

(d) **Aqueous Fe^{2+} ions react with aqueous hydroxide ions. Write an ionic equation**
for this reaction and state what you would see. (2 marks)

(e) **The product formed when aqueous Fe^{2+} ions react with aqueous hydroxide ions**
slowly darkens and eventually turns 'rusty'. Explain this observation. (2 marks)

Total: 9 marks

■ ■ ■

Candidates' answers to Question 2

Candidate A
(a) An element that forms one or more stable ions that have partly filled *d*-orbitals.

Candidate B
(a) An element that has partly filled *d*-orbitals.

e Candidate A gets both marks but Candidate B only scores 1 mark. There are two key
marking points. Partly filled *d*-orbitals is essential for 1 mark. The second mark is for
stating that the element forms one or more *ions* that have partly filled *d*-orbitals.

Candidate A
(b) $1s^2 2s^2 2p^6 3s^2 3p^6 3d^6 4s^2$

Candidate B
(b) $1s^2 2s^2 2p^6 3s^2 3p^6 4s^2 3d^6$

e Both candidates gain the mark, but Candidate A's is the better response because it is
easier to deduce the electronic configuration of any resulting ions.

Candidate A
(c) Fe^{2+} — $1s^2 2s^2 2p^6 3s^2 3p^6 3d^6$
Fe^{3+} — $1s^2 2s^2 2p^6 3s^2 3p^6 3d^5$

Candidate B
(c) Fe^{2+} — $1s^2 2s^2 2p^6 3s^2 3p^6 4s^2 3d^4$
Fe^{3+} — $1s^2 2s^2 2p^6 3s^2 3p^6 4s^2 3d^3$

e Candidate A gains both marks but Candidate B fails to score. The way in which
Candidate B wrote the Fe atom configuration in (b) reflects that the 4s sub-shell fills
before the 3d sub-shell. However, the danger of writing it in this way is that when ions
are formed, the tendency is to remove electrons from the 3d orbitals first, when in fact

question

the first electrons to be lost are always the outer electrons — in this case, the electrons in the fourth shell.

Candidate A

(d) $Fe^{2+}(aq) + 2OH^-(aq) \longrightarrow Fe(OH)_2(s)$
Green precipitate

Candidate B

(d) $Fe^{2+}(aq) + 2OH^-(aq) \longrightarrow Fe(OH)_2(s)$
$Fe(OH)_2$ is a blue-green gelatinous precipitate.

e Both candidates score 2 marks.

Candidate A

(e) Fe^{3+} is more stable than Fe^{2+} because the electronic configuration of Fe^{3+} has a half-full d shell, $3d^5$, which is more stable than Fe^{2+}. The rust colour is due to $Fe(OH)_3$ being formed.

Candidate B

(e) $Fe(OH)_3$ is a rust-brown gelatinous precipitate. Therefore, $Fe(OH)_2$ must have changed to $Fe(OH)_3$.

e Candidate A gains both marks. Candidate B scores 1 mark for stating that Fe^{3+} is formed but loses a mark for not attempting to explain why.

e **Candidate A scores full marks and Candidate B scores 5 out of 9 marks. The marks lost by Candidate B centre around the response to (b). If the electronic configuration of the iron atom had been written as $1s^22s^22p^63s^23p^63d^64s^2$ instead of $1s^22s^22p^63s^23p^64s^23d^6$, 2 more marks would probably have been scored in (c). Also, the candidate could have spotted that Fe^{3+} has a half-filled d shell and been able to explain the stability of Fe^{3+} in (e).**

uestion

Colour

The visible spectrum of transition metal ion compound **X** is shown below.

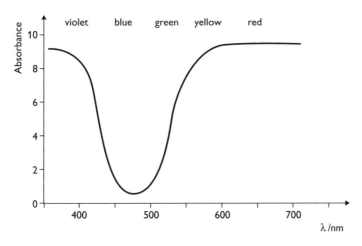

(a) (i) Predict the colour of **X**.   (1 mark)
    (ii) Justify your prediction.   (2 marks)
(b) Potassium manganate(VII), **KMnO₄**, is often used in redox titrations.
    The manganate(VII) ion, MnO_4^-(aq), has a distinctive colour.
    (i) State the colour of the MnO_4^-(aq) ion.   (1 mark)
    (ii) Predict the visible spectrum of the MnO_4^-(aq) ion by sketching it on the
         grid below.   (2 marks)

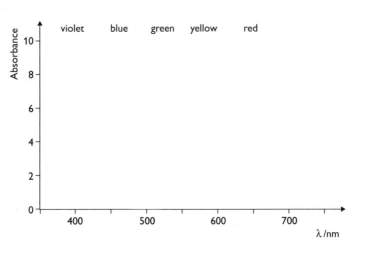

Total: 6 marks

question 3

Candidates' answers to Question 3

Candidate A

(a) (i) Green

Candidate B

(a) (i) Red-violet

e Candidate A gains the mark. Candidate B does not score because the spectrum has been misinterpreted.

Candidate A

(a) (ii) The violet and the red parts of the spectrum have been absorbed which means that the blue, green and yellow will be transmitted. Blue, green and yellow will produce a green colour, which is what we will see.

Candidate B

(a) (ii) Blue, green and yellow are absorbed, hence we see a combination of violet and red.

e Candidate A gives a textbook answer and gains both marks. Candidate B explains the answer to (a)(i) but is confused about which parts of the spectrum have been absorbed. The only error is misinterpretation of the spectrum, which has already been penalised. This initial error is taken into account when marking (a)(ii). Candidate B would certainly gain 1 mark, possibly even 2.

Candidate A

(b) (i) Purple

Candidate B

(b) (i) Orange

e Candidate A scores the mark. Candidate B loses an easy mark by confusing potassium manganate(VII) with potassium dichromate.

Candidate A

(b) (ii)

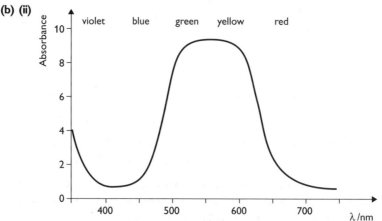

Candidate B

(b) (ii)

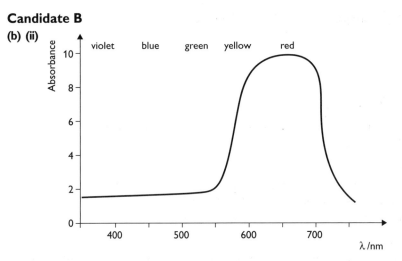

Candidate A gives another very good answer. The answer clearly shows that the blue and red parts of the spectrum are *not* absorbed. Since blue and red make purple, Candidate A scores both marks. Candidate B's spectrum would be marked consequentially, taking into account the incorrect answer to (b)(i). However, the spectrum has again been misinterpreted, and absorbance and transmission have been confused. The underlying principle is illustrated below.

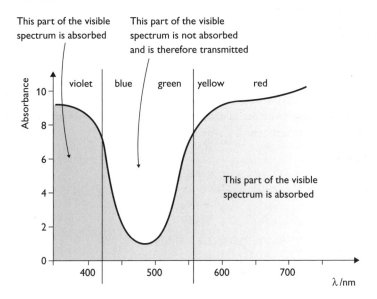

The violet, yellow and red parts of the visible spectrum are absorbed and the blue-green part of the spectrum is transmitted. Hence, we see a combination of blue-green.

Candidate A scores maximum marks. Candidate B achieves only 2 or 3 out of 6 marks. The main fault with candidate B's response is confusion between absorbance and transmission in the visible spectrum.

Redox titrations

The dichromate ion, $Cr_2O_7^{2-}$, is an oxidising agent which is used in laboratory analysis. It reacts with acidified Fe^{2+} ions to form Cr^{3+} and Fe^{3+} ions:

$$Cr_2O_7^{2-} + 14H^+ + 6e^- \longrightarrow 2Cr^{3+} + 7H_2O$$
$$Fe^{2+} \longrightarrow Fe^{3+} + e^-$$

(a) Construct the full ionic equation for this reaction. (1 mark)

(b) Calculate the volume of $0.0100\ mol\,dm^{-3}$ potassium dichromate required to react with $20.0\ cm^3$ of $0.0500\ mol\,dm^{-3}$ acidified iron(II) sulphate. (3 marks)

(c) Fe^{3+} forms complex ions such as $Fe(H_2O)_6^{3+}$ in which water acts as a ligand by forming coordinate bonds. Explain the meaning of the terms *complex ion*, *ligand* and *coordinate bond*. (3 marks)

(d) When thiocyanate ions, SCN^-, are added to $Fe(H_2O)_6^{3+}$, a ligand–ligand exchange reaction occurs. Write an equation for this reaction and state what you would see. (2 marks)

Total: 9 marks

Candidates' answers to Question 4

Candidate A

(a) $Cr_2O_7^{2-} + 14H^+ + 6Fe^{2+} \longrightarrow 6Fe^{3+} + 2Cr^{3+} + 7H_2O$

Candidate B

(a) $Cr_2O_7^{2-} + 14H^+ + 5e^- + Fe^{2+} \longrightarrow Fe^{3+} + 2Cr^{3+} + 7H_2O$

📝 Candidate A gains the mark but Candidate B does not score. The full ionic equation does not contain any electrons. It is essential to scale the two half-ionic equations so that the electrons cancel out.

Candidate A

(b) Moles of $Fe^{2+} = 0.0500 \times 20.0/1000 = 0.001\ mol$
Moles of $Cr_2O_7^{2-} = 6 \times$ moles of $Fe^{2+} = 0.001 \times 6 = 0.006\ mol$
$n = cV$
Therefore, $V = n/c$
Volume of $Cr_2O_7^{2-} = 0.006/0.01 = 0.6 = 600\ cm^3$

Candidate B

(b) Moles of Fe^{2+} = moles of $Cr_2O_7^{2-} = 0.0500 \times 20.0/1000 = 0.001\ mol$
$n = cV$
Therefore, $V = n/c = 0.001/0.01 = 0.1\ dm^3 = 100\ cm^3$

📝 Both candidates score 2 marks out of 3, but for different reasons. Candidate A has correctly calculated the moles of Fe^{2+} but has multiplied this value by 6 instead of dividing it by 6. Candidate B has calculated the moles of Fe^{2+} correctly, but has not used the 1:6 molar ratio at all. Both candidates have gone on to calculate the volume of $Cr_2O_7{}^{2-}$ required. Both display good examination technique by showing their working. Titration calculations are usually designed so that the volume added from the burette is around $25\,cm^3$. Examination questions reflect this, such that burette values will not exceed $50\,cm^3$. The answers obtained by both candidates should have prompted them to check their calculations for errors. The correct value is $16.7\,cm^3$.

Candidate A
(c) A complex ion contains six water molecules.

A ligand is a lone pair donor.

A coordinate bond is the same as a dative bond — the ligand supplies both electrons.

Candidate B
(c) A complex ion is not as simple as an ion such as Cl^-.

A ligand is a lone pair donor.

A coordinate bond is formed between the ligand and the vacant d-orbitals of the Fe^{2+}. The ligand supplies both electrons for the bond.

e Both candidates score 2 marks. Neither has explained what is meant by the term 'complex ion'. A complex ion is best defined as a central transition metal ion surrounded by ligands.

Candidate A
(d) $Fe(H_2O)_6{}^{3+} + SCN^- \longrightarrow Fe(H_2O)_5SCN^{3+} + H_2O$

Blood-red colour

Candidate B
(d) $Fe(H_2O)_6{}^{3+} + 6SCN^- \longrightarrow Fe(SCN)_6{}^{3-} + 6H_2O$

Bright red complex

e Both candidates gain 1 mark for the observation, but neither scores the mark for the correct equation. The complex formed is $Fe(H_2O)_5SCN^{2+}$. Candidate A is almost correct but has not balanced the Fe^{3+} and SCN^- charges. Candidate B has balanced the charges but the stoichiometry is wrong.

e **This was not a very good question for either candidate. Candidate A scores 6 out of 9 marks and Candidate B scores 5 marks. Both candidates are around the C/D borderline as a result of some careless errors.**

Question 5

Period 3

(a) Describe, with the aid of equations, how sodium and phosphorus react with oxygen and with chlorine. (8 marks)

(b) Describe, with the aid of equations, the action of water, if any, on the oxides and chlorides of sodium and phosphorus. (8 marks)

In this question, 1 mark is available for the quality of written communication. (1 mark)

Total: 17 marks

■ ■ ■

Candidates' answers to Question 5

Candidate A

(a) Sodium reacts vigorously with both oxygen and with chlorine. Phosphorus is stored under water because it catches fire when in contact with oxygen. The equations for the reactions are:

$$4Na + O_2 \longrightarrow 2Na_2O$$
$$2Na + Cl_2 \longrightarrow 2NaCl$$
$$4P + 5O_2 \longrightarrow 2P_2O_5$$
$$2P + 5Cl_2 \longrightarrow 2PCl_5$$

Candidate B

(a) $4Na + O_2 \longrightarrow 2Na_2O$

Burns with a yellow flame to form a white solid

$2Na + Cl_2 \longrightarrow 2NaCl$

Burns with a yellow flame to form a white solid

$4P + 5O_2 \longrightarrow 2P_2O_5$

Burns with a white flame to form a white solid

$2P + 5Cl_2 \longrightarrow 2PCl_5$

Burns with a white flame to form a white solid

e Before answering the question, it is worth looking at the mark allocation and trying to deduce where the marks will be allocated. There are two elements, Na and P, each reacting with oxygen and with chlorine. Therefore, it is reasonable to assume that there will be 1 mark for each equation and 1 mark for each observation. To score a mark for quality of written communication, you do not have to write much. Often as little as two consecutive sentences is enough, but you *must* attempt to write in continuous prose. Candidate B has adopted a very systematic approach and scores 6 marks. The first three equations and observations are all correct. Candidate A has been less systematic but has attempted to write an introduction in continuous prose and may get the mark for quality of written communication. Candidate A also gains 3 marks for the equations. However, the observations are vague and score only 1 mark. Both candidates have made an error in describing the reaction of phosphorus with chlorine. PCl_3 is formed, not PCl_5. In the presence of Cl_2, phosphorus burns with a pale green flame to form PCl_3. PCl_5 is only stable at low temperatures and is prepared by passing Cl_2 over PCl_3 under ice-cold conditions.

Candidate A

(b) Sodium oxide reacts with water to form sodium hydroxide. Sodium chloride simply dissolves in water. Phosphorus oxide and chloride react violently with water. The equations for the reactions are:

$$Na_2O + H_2O \longrightarrow 2NaOH$$
$$NaCl(s) \longrightarrow NaCl(aq) \longrightarrow Na^+(aq) + Cl^-(aq)$$
$$P_2O_5 + 3H_2O \longrightarrow 2H_3PO_4$$
$$PCl_5 + 4H_2O \longrightarrow H_3PO_4 + 5HCl$$

Candidate B

(b) $\quad Na_2O + H_2O \longrightarrow 2NaOH$
Exothermic reaction

$\quad NaCl + H_2O \longrightarrow NaOH + HCl$
Exothermic reaction

$\quad P_2O_5 + 3H_2O \longrightarrow 2H_3PO_4$
Violent reaction

$\quad PCl_5 + 4H_2O \longrightarrow H_3PO_4 + 5HCl$
Violent reaction and misty white fumes given off

e Candidate A scores 4 marks for the reactions, which are all correct. However, the observations are weak and earn 2 marks only. Candidate B has adopted the same systematic approach as earlier, and scores well. Three sets of equations and observations are correct, so Candidate B scores 6 marks. Candidate B has incorrectly suggested that NaCl reacts with water to produce NaOH and HCl. Many candidates fall into this trap and seem afraid to state that there is no reaction or that NaCl simply dissolves. Candidate A gains the mark for quality of written communication but Candidate B does not. In order to earn this mark you must use some continuous prose. Candidate A has tried to do this; Candidate B has made no attempt. However, when trying to write chemistry in continuous prose it is easy to forget some of the essential detail.

e **Overall, Candidate A scores 11 marks. Marks were lost by not fully describing the observations. By contrast, the systematic approach adopted by Candidate B results in a total of 12 marks.**

uestion 6

Rate equations

The reaction between hydrogen and nitrogen monoxide is a redox reaction which results in the formation of nitrogen and water.

(a) (i) Write a balanced equation for the reaction.   (1 mark)

    (ii) Identify the oxidising agent in the reaction. Justify your answer.   (2 marks)

The rate equation for the reaction is:

rate = $k[H_2(g)][NO(g)]^2$

(b) Using 1.2×10^{-2} mol dm^{-3} $H_2(g)$ and 6.0×10^{-3} mol dm^{-3} NO(g), the initial rate of this reaction was 3.6×10^{-2} mol dm^{-3} s^{-1}. Calculate the rate constant, k, for this reaction. Quote your answer to 2 significant figures. State the units of the rate constant, k.   (4 marks)

(c) Calculate the initial rate of reaction when each of the following changes is made. Show your working.

    (i) The concentration of the H_2 is tripled.   (1 mark)

    (ii) The concentration of the NO is halved.   (1 mark)

    (iii) The concentration of both is doubled.   (1 mark)

(d) Dinitrogen pentoxide decomposes according to the equation:

    $2N_2O_5(g) \longrightarrow 4NO_2(g) + O_2(g)$

The decomposition is a first-order reaction with respect to $N_2O_5(g)$. This decomposition proceeds by a two-step mechanism with the rate-determining step taking place first.

    (i) Write a rate equation for this reaction.   (1 mark)

    (ii) Explain the term *rate-determining step*.   (1 mark)

    (iii) Suggest the two steps for this reaction and write their equations. Show clearly that the two steps equate to the balanced equation given above.   (3 marks)

Total: 15 marks

■ ■ ■

Candidates' answers to Question 6

Candidate A

(a) (i) $2H_2 + 2NO \longrightarrow N_2 + 2H_2O$

Candidate B

(a) (i) $H_2 + NO \longrightarrow \frac{1}{2}N_2 + H_2O$

🖉 Both are correct. The equation must be balanced and it is acceptable to use fractions.

Candidate A

(a) (ii)

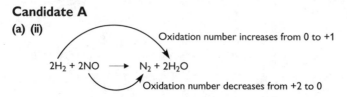

The H_2 has been oxidised because its oxidation number has increased. Therefore, the NO must have been the oxidising agent.

Candidate B

(a) (ii) NO

e There are only two possible answers. The oxidising agent must be either H_2 or NO, so there is a 50:50 chance of guessing the answer. When questions like this are asked, there are usually no marks for the correct answer. The marks are awarded for the explanation. Both candidates have given the correct answer but Candidate B has given no explanation and so scores no marks. The explanation given by Candidate A scores both marks.

Candidate A

(b) Rate = $k[H_2(g)][NO(g)]^2$
$3.6 \times 10^{-2} = k(1.2 \times 10^{-2})(6.0 \times 10^{-3})^2$
$3.6 \times 10^{-2} = k(1.2 \times 10^{-2})(3.6 \times 10^{-5})$
$3.6 \times 10^{-2} = k(4.32 \times 10^{-7})$
$k = 3.6 \times 10^{-2}/(4.32 \times 10^{-7}) = 83333.3 = 8.3 \times 10^4$

Candidate B

(b) $k = 83333.3$

e Both candidates have calculated the correct numerical value but neither has quoted the units for k and both, therefore, lose a mark. The question also asks for the answer to 2 significant figures. Candidate B has ignored this and loses another mark. Candidate A scores 3 out of 4 marks and Candidate B scores 2 marks.

Candidate A

(c) (i) The rate triples.

Candidate B

(c) (i) The rate triples.

e Both candidates score the mark.

Candidate A

(c) (ii) The rate is twice as slow.

Candidate B

(c) (ii) The rate is half as fast.

e Neither candidate is correct. If the concentration of NO is halved, then the rate will change by a factor of $(\frac{1}{2})^2 = \frac{1}{4}$.

Candidate A

(c) (iii) The rate is four times as fast.

Candidate B

(c) (iii) The rate is eight times as fast.

e Candidate B gains the mark. Overall, the reaction is third-order and if both concentrations are doubled, the rate will change by a factor of $2^3 = 8$. Candidate A does not score.

Candidate A

(d) (i) Rate = $k[N_2O_5]$

Candidate B

(d) (i) Rate = $[N_2O_5]$

e Candidate A gains the mark. Candidate B has forgotten to include the rate constant, k, and loses the mark.

Candidate A

(d) (ii) The slowest step in the mechanism

Candidate B

(d) (ii) The slowest step

e Both candidates gain the mark.

Candidate A

(d) (iii) Slow step (rate-determining step): $1N_2O_5 \longrightarrow 2NO_2 + O$
Fast step: $O + 1N_2O_5 \longrightarrow 2NO_2 + O_2$
Balanced equation: $2N_2O_5 \longrightarrow 4NO_2 + O_2$

Candidate B

(d) (iii) $1N_2O_5 \longrightarrow N_2O_3 + O_2$
$N_2O_3 + 1N_2O_5 \longrightarrow 4NO_2$
$2N_2O_5 \longrightarrow 4NO_2 + O_2$

e Candidates find devising mechanisms difficult. However, both candidates have given good answers, scoring full marks. The exact mechanism is not relevant, but both candidates have used the information in the question to suggest valid alternatives.

e **Overall, Candidate A scores 12 out of 15 marks which is grade-A standard. Candidate B scores 9, which equates to a grade C. With a little more care and better examination technique, this could easily have become grade-A standard.**

Question 7

pH

(a) A weak organic acid, HA, with a relative molecular mass of 60, has the following percentage composition by mass: C, 40.0%; H, 6.7%; O, 53.3%. Calculate the molecular formula of HA. (3 marks)

(b) 1.20 g of HA was dissolved in 250 cm^3 water. Calculate the pH of the resulting solution. Show *all* your working. (K_a of HA = 1.7×10^{-5} mol dm^{-3}) (6 marks)

(c) A 0.04 mol dm^{-3} solution of HA was titrated with a 0.05 mol dm^{-3} sodium hydroxide solution.

(i) Calculate the pH of the NaOH(aq). ($K_w = 1.0 \times 10^{-14}$ mol^2 dm^{-6}) (2 marks)

(ii) Calculate the volume of NaOH(aq) required to neutralise 25.0 cm^3 of HA solution. (3 marks)

(iii) Sketch a graph to show the change in pH during the titration. (4 marks)

(d) Indicators can be used to determine the end point of a titration. Which of the following would be most suitable for this titration? Justify your answer and suggest what you would see at the end point. (3 marks)

Indicator	Acid colour	pH range	Alkaline colour
Thymol blue (acid)	Red	1.2–2.8	Yellow
Bromocresol purple	Yellow	5.0–6.8	Purple
Thymol blue (base)	Yellow	8.0–9.6	Blue

Total: 21 marks

■ ■ ■

Candidates' answers to Question 7

Candidate A

(a)

	Carbon	Hydrogen	Oxygen
% composition	40.0	6.7	53.3
A_r	12	1	16
Divide by A_r	3.33	6.7	3.33
Divide by smallest	1	2	1

Empirical formula = CH_2O
CH_2O has a mass = 12 + 2 + 16 = 30
Empirical mass × 2 = molecular mass
Molecular formula = $C_2H_4O_2$

Candidate B

(a) Molecular formula = $C_2H_4O_2$

📝 Both candidates score 3 marks. However, Candidate B shows poor examination technique. It is always advisable to show your working. If Candidate B had made an error, all 3 marks would have been lost.

Candidate A

(b) $K_a = \dfrac{[H^+][A^-]}{[HA]} = \dfrac{[H^+]^2}{[HA]}$

Therefore $[H^+]^2 = K_a \times [HA]$

$K_a = 1.7 \times 10^{-5}$

$[HA] = 1.2/60 = 0.02$

Therefore, $[H^+]^2 = 1.7 \times 10^{-5} \times 0.02 = 3.4 \times 10^{-7}$

$H^+ = \sqrt{(3.4 \times 10^{-7})} = 5.8 \times 10^{-4}$

$pH = -\log_{10}[H^+] = -\log_{10}(5.8 \times 10^{-4}) = 3.23$

Candidate B

(b) $pH = -\log 10\sqrt{(K_a \times [HA])}$

$pH = 4.69$

📝 Questions like this are extremely difficult to mark because there are a number of equally valid ways of carrying out the calculation. The instructions ask the candidates to show *all* their working. Neither candidate has the correct answer of pH = 2.93. However, Candidate A scores 5 out of 6 marks, while candidate B only scores 1 mark. Candidate A has shown all the working, so it is possible to see where mistakes have been made. The only error is in working out the HA concentration. By using the value 1.2/60 = 0.02, Candidate A has worked out the number of moles of HA rather than the concentration. The correct concentration is $0.08 \, mol \, dm^{-3}$. It is impossible to deduce where candidate B has gone wrong. The only mark that can be awarded is for quoting the equation $pH = -\log \sqrt{(K_a \times [HA])}$, which could be used to obtain the correct answer. Try the calculation; remember, $K_a = 1.7 \times 10^{-5}$ and $[HA] = 0.08$.

Candidate A

(c) (i) $K_w = [H^+][OH^-] = 1.0 \times 10^{-14}$

$[H^+][0.05] = 1.0 \times 10^{-14}$

Therefore, $[H^+] = 1.0 \times 10^{-14}/0.05 = 2.0 \times 10^{-13}$

$pH = -\log_{10}[H^+] = -\log_{10}(2.0 \times 10^{-13}) = 12.7$

Candidate B

(c) (i) $pOH = -\log_{10}[OH^-] = -\log_{10}(0.05) = 1.30$

$pH = 14 - pOH = 14 - 1.30 = 12.7$

📝 Both candidates score 2 marks. The methods adopted are different but both are valid and lead to the correct answer.

Candidate A

(c) (ii) $HA + NaOH \longrightarrow NaA + H_2O$

Moles of HA = moles of NaOH

$n = cV = 0.04 \times 25/1000 = 0.001$

Volume of NaOH = $V = n/c = 0.001/0.05 = 0.02 \, dm^3 = 20 \, cm^3$

Candidate B

(c) (ii) $20\,cm^3$

e Both candidates score all 3 marks but Candidate B is living dangerously again. It is vital to show your working in any calculation. Throughout this question, Candidate B has not done this. It can be very costly in terms of lost marks.

Candidate A

(c) (iii)

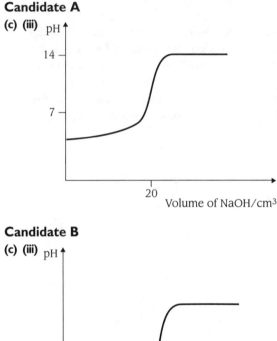

Candidate B

(c) (iii)

Volume of NaOH/cm³

e The marking points for the sketch are: correct labels including units ✓; initial and final pH approximately correct ✓; correct shape ✓; rapid change in pH from about 7–12, after the addition of $20\,cm^3$ of NaOH ✓. Candidate A is methodical and gains all 4 marks. Candidate B also understands the chemistry but only scores 1 mark. Use the mark scheme above to see if you can identify where Candidate B has lost 3 marks.

Candidate A

(d) Thymol blue (base) would be the best indicator because it changes colour in the pH region 8.0–9.6, which matches the rapid change in pH for this reaction.

Candidate B

(d) Thymol blue (base) would be the best indicator because it changes colour in the pH region 8.0–9.6. The end point would be a green colour.

question

e Both candidates have selected the correct indicator. Candidate A gives a very good explanation of the choice of thymol blue (base) but has forgotten to give the colour of the end point. Candidate B has not really explained the choice of indicator and has simply copied the pH range from the question. The end point should occur when there is an equal amount of the acid and alkaline forms of the indicator, i.e. an equal amount of yellow and blue. Hence the end point would be green. Both candidates score 2 marks.

e **Both candidates seem to understand the chemistry but Candidate B demonstrates poor examination technique throughout the question. The net result of this poor technique is that Candidate B is underachieving by two to three grades. Look back at Candidate B's responses and identify marks that should have been gained. Candidate A scores 19 out of 21 marks, which is grade-A standard. Candidate B achieves 12 marks out of 21, which equates to a grade D.**

Equilibrium

Hydrogen and iodine react according to the equation:

$$H_2(g) + I_2(g) \rightleftharpoons 2HI(g) \qquad \Delta H = +53.0 \, kJ \, mol^{-1}$$

(a) State Le Chatelier's principle. (1 mark)

(b) Use Le Chatelier's principle to predict what happens to the position of the equilibrium when:
(i) the temperature is increased
(ii) the pressure is increased
(iii) a catalyst is used
Justify each of your predictions. (6 marks)

(c) Write an expression for K_c for the equilibrium. State the units, if any. (2 marks)

(d) When 0.18 moles of I_2 and 0.50 moles of H_2 were placed in a 500 cm³ sealed container and allowed to reach equilibrium, the equilibrium mixture was found to contain 0.010 moles of I_2. Calculate K_c. (5 marks)

Total: 14 marks

■ ■ ■

Candidates' answers to Question 8

Candidate A

(a) When a system at equilibrium is subjected to a change, the system will move to try to minimise the effect of the change.

Candidate B

(a) When a system at equilibrium is subjected to a change in external conditions, the system will move to cancel the effect of the change.

e Candidate A scores the mark but Candidate B doesn't. Le Chatelier's principle clearly states that the system responds to changes by trying to *minimise* the effect of that change. It *cannot* cancel out the change.

Candidate A

(b) (i) The equilibrium moves to the right because it favours the endothermic forward reaction.

Candidate B

(b) (i) More HI will be produced because it is an endothermic forward reaction.

e Both candidates are correct, for 2 marks.

Candidate A

(b) (ii) No effect, because there are an equal number of molecules of gas on both sides.

Candidate B

(b) (ii) It speeds up the reaction because it increases the chances of collision.

e Candidate A is correct, for 2 marks. Candidate B scores no marks because the answer relates to the rate of reaction, *not* the position of equilibrium.

Candidate A

(b) (iii) It speeds up the reaction and the catalyst remains unchanged at the end of the reaction.

Candidate B

(b) (iii) It speeds up the reaction by lowering the activation energy.

e Candidate A has not predicted the position of the equilibrium and the explanation is not relevant to the question. No marks are awarded. Again, Candidate B scores no marks because the answer relates to the rate of reaction and not the position of equilibrium.

Candidate A

(c) $K_c = \dfrac{[HI]^2}{[H_2][I_2]}$

There are no units.

Candidate B

(c) $K_c = \dfrac{[HI]^2}{[H_2][I_2]}$

There are no units.

e Both candidates gain 2 marks.

Candidate A

(d) $H_2(g) + I_2(g) \rightleftharpoons 2HI(g)$

Initial moles: H_2, 0.50; I_2, 0.18; HI, 0

Final moles: $0.010 \, mol$ of I_2 remain. Therefore, it follows that $0.17 \, mol$ of I_2 and $0.17 \, mol$ of H_2 also reacted. Hence the moles of H_2 left $= 0.50 - 0.17 = 0.33 \, mol$.

For each mole of I_2 and H_2 that reacts, 2 mol of HI are formed. Therefore, the equilibrium amount of HI $= 2 \times 0.17 = 0.34 \, mol$. K_c is measured in terms of concentration and so each of the equilibrium amounts must be converted to $mol \, dm^{-3}$.

$I_2 = 0.01/0.5 = 0.02 \, mol \, dm^{-3}$

$H_2 = 0.33/0.5 = 0.66 \, mol \, dm^{-3}$

$HI = 0.34/0.5 = 0.68 \, mol \, dm^{-3}$

Therefore, $K_c = \dfrac{0.68}{0.02 \times 0.66} = 51.5$

Candidate B

(d) $K_c = \dfrac{[HI]^2}{[H_2][I_2]}$

$= \dfrac{(0.34)^2}{(0.33)(0.01)} = 35$

e Both candidates are awarded 4 out of 5 marks even though Candidate A has the wrong final answer. Candidate A shows good examination technique by showing all the working. All the steps are correct, except for forgetting to square the equilibrium value of [HI] in the final input into K_c. Again, Candidate B has not shown all the working, but shows enough to demonstrate that the calculation has been worked through fully. The values used should always be the concentration, in mol dm^{-3}, for each chemical. Candidate B has used mole values. In this particular calculation, the numerical value is the same whether moles or mol dm^{-3} are used, but this is not always the case.

e **Overall, Candidate A scores 11 out of 14 marks which equates to a grade B. Candidate B scores 8 marks, which is on the C/D borderline.**

Acids and bases

A patient suffering from a duodenal ulcer displays increased acidity in his gastric juices. The exact acidity of the patient's gastric juice is monitored by measuring the pH.

(a) (i) Define pH. (1 mark)

(ii) The patient's gastric juice was found to have a hydrochloric acid concentration of $8.0 \times 10^{-2}\,mol\,dm^{-3}$. Calculate the pH of the gastric juice. (1 mark)

One of the most common medications designed for the relief of excess stomach acidity is aluminium hydroxide, $Al(OH)_3$.

(b) (i) Write an equation for the reaction between HCl and $Al(OH)_3$. (1 mark)

(ii) The patient produces $2.00\,dm^3$ of gastric juices per day. The $Al(OH)_3$ is taken in solution at a concentration of $1.25\,mol\,dm^{-3}$. Calculate the minimum volume of $Al(OH)_3$ solution required daily. (5 marks)

Total: 8 marks

■ ■ ■

Candidates' answers to Question 9

Candidate A

(a) (i) $pH = -log_{10}[H^+(aq)]$

Candidate B

(a) (i) $pH = -log_{10}[H^+]$

e Both candidates score the mark.

Candidate A

(a) (ii) $pH = -log_{10}(8.0 \times 10^{-2}) = 1.10$

Candidate B

(a) (ii) $pH = 1.097$

e Both candidates score the mark.

Candidate A

(b) (i) $3HCl + Al(OH)_3 \longrightarrow AlCl_3 + 3H_2O$

Candidate B

(b) (i) $3HCl + Al(OH)_3 \longrightarrow AlCl_3 + 3H_2O$

e Again, both candidates score the mark.

Candidate A

(b) (ii) $3HCl + Al(OH)_3 \longrightarrow AlCl_3 + 3H_2O$

Mole ratio: 3 moles HCl react with 1 mole $Al(OH)_3$

Moles of HCl = concentration × volume = $(8.0 \times 10^{-2}) \times 2.00 = 0.16$

Therefore, moles of $Al(OH)_3 = 3 \times 0.16 = 0.48$

Volume of $Al(OH)_3$ = moles/concentration = $0.48/1.25 = 0.384 = 384\,cm^3$

Candidate B

(b) (ii) $3HCl + Al(OH)_3 \longrightarrow AlCl_3 + 3H_2O$

 $384\,cm^3$

ℰ Both candidates have the same answer, which is incorrect. The correct value is $42.7\,cm^3$. However, the outcomes are very different. Candidate A scores 4 out of 5 marks, while Candidate B scores zero. The examiner can only mark what is written on the paper. Candidate B has elected not to show any working, so the only thing to mark is the answer — which is incorrect. As Candidate A has shown the working, it is possible for the marker to identify when the error occurred and to follow it through the rest of the calculation.

ℰ **Candidate A correctly worked out the moles of HCl but calculated the moles of Al(OH)₃ incorrectly. The ratio is 3 moles HCl ≡ 1 mole Al(OH)₃ and hence Candidate A should have divided by 3 instead of multiplying by 3.**

Both candidates gave the same answers to all parts of this question but Candidate A scored 7 marks out of 8 while Candidate B scored only 3 marks. It is all down to exam technique. Candidate A showed his/her working and Candidate B did not.

Synoptic question

Copper reacts with nitric acid, HNO_3. The products depend on the concentration of the acid.

Copper + dilute nitric acid:

$Cu(s) \longrightarrow Cu^{2+}(aq) + 2e^-$

$4H^+(aq) + NO_3^-(aq) + 3e^- \longrightarrow NO(g) + 2H_2O(l)$

Copper + concentrated nitric acid:

$Cu(s) \longrightarrow Cu^{2+}(aq) + 2e^-$

$2H^+(aq) + NO_3^-(aq) + 1e^- \longrightarrow NO_2(g) + H_2O(l)$

When nitric acid reacts with 1.27 g of copper, 320 cm³ of gas is produced. Write balanced equations for each reaction and deduce whether the acid is dilute or concentrated. Show *all* your working.

9 marks

■ ■ ■

Candidates' answers to Question 10

Candidate A

The electrons have to balance.

Dilute acid:

$Cu(s) \longrightarrow Cu^{2+}(aq) + 2e^-$

Multiply by 3

$3Cu(s) \longrightarrow 3Cu^{2+}(aq) + 6e^-$

$4H^+(aq) + NO_3^-(aq) + 3e^- \longrightarrow NO(g) + 2H_2O(l)$

Multiply by 2

$8H^+(aq) + 2NO_3^-(aq) + 6e^- \longrightarrow 2NO(g) + 4H_2O(l)$

Add the resulting equations.

Balanced equation: $8H^+(aq) + 2NO_3^-(aq) + 3Cu(s) \longrightarrow 3Cu^{2+}(aq) + 2NO(g) + 4H_2O(l)$

This shows that 3 moles of Cu produce 2 moles of NO(g).

Concentrated acid:

$2H^+(aq) + NO_3^-(aq) + 1e^- \longrightarrow NO_2(g) + H_2O(l)$

Multiply by 2

$4H^+(aq) + 2NO_3^-(aq) + 2e^- \longrightarrow NO_2(g) + H_2O(l)$

Add to:

$Cu(s) \longrightarrow Cu^{2+}(aq) + 2e^-$

Balanced equation: $4H^+(aq) + 2NO_3^-(aq) + Cu(s) \longrightarrow Cu^{2+}(aq) + NO_2(g) + H_2O(l)$

This shows that 1 mole of Cu produces 1 mole of $NO_2(g)$.

The number of moles of copper reacted is $1.27/63.5 = 0.02$

The number of moles of gas produced is $320/24000 = 0.0133$

	Copper	Gas
Mole ratio	0.02	0.0133
Divide by smallest	1.5	1
Whole numbers	3	2

3 moles of Cu produce 2 moles of gas and therefore the acid must be dilute.

Candidate B

Dilute nitric: $8H^+(aq) + 2NO_3^-(aq) + 3Cu(s) \longrightarrow 3Cu^{2+}(aq) + 2NO(g) + 4H_2O(l)$

Conc. nitric: $4H^+(aq) + 2NO_3^-(aq) + Cu(s) \longrightarrow Cu^{2+}(aq) + 2NO_2(g) + 2H_2O(l)$

Moles of Cu used $= 0.02$

Moles of gas $= 320/24 = 13.3$

✒ For the dilute acid equations, the marking points are: multiply the copper half-equation by 3 ✓; multiply the acid half-equation by 2 ✓; correct balanced equation ✓. For the concentrated acid equations, the marking points are: multiply the acid half-equation by 2 ✓; correct balanced equation ✓. The remaining points are: moles of copper used ✓; moles of gas produced ✓; mole ratio of copper to gas ✓; relating the mole ratio to the correct equation ✓. Candidate A scores all 3 marks for the dilute acid equations but carelessly loses 2 marks for the concentrated acid equations. Candidate A scores the final 4 marks by deducing correctly that the dilute acid was used. Candidate B poses a real dilemma for the examiner. Clearly, Candidate B is very able and has deduced the balanced equations for both reactions correctly. However, there is no working. Candidate B would probably gain 4 of the 5 marks available for the equations. Candidate B scores 1 mark for the moles of copper used but scores no further marks. In the final part of the calculation, Candidate B divides $320\,cm^3$ by $24\,dm^3$, which is incorrect. The value obtained does not relate to either equation and so the candidate is unable to continue the calculation.

✒ Overall, **Candidate A scores 7 out of 9 marks even though one of the equations is wrong. Candidate B deduced both equations correctly but only scores 5 marks.**